Exploring 6 – 10

BEV DUNBAR

Blake
EDUCATION
Better ways to learn

Introduction

EXPLORING 6-10

At last! Here are over 100 fun, easy-to-use and easy-to-understand early number activities, with sample programs, blackline masters and assessment pages to make your teaching life easier! All exploring just the numbers from 6-10!

The resources for each number include flashcards and original rhymes followed by a variety of exciting, practical activities for the whole class, groups, pairs or individuals.

By exploring each number for a week at a time, as shown in the sample program, you will be able to cater for at least three ability groups, with plenty to challenge all your students. And the wide range of activities means that every number is treated in a different way. You'll never run out of ideas again!

As intelligent, fun-loving, active five year olds, your students probably know the basic ideas, but could further develop their understanding of each number through games, activities and social interaction with their friends. Through problem-solving and working with others, your students will learn to inquire and estimate, see patterns and relationships and use different strategies.

This is Book 2 in the three volume Early Number Kit. Together with the other two books, "Exploring 1-5" and "Number Games and Activities for 0-10", you will have a complete teaching resource for numbers to 10.

In fact, there are more than enough number ideas here to keep both you and your students keen and motivated year after year.

And if you think this book, Exploring 6-10, is useful, then why not collect the other two books as well!

Copyright © Bev Dunbar MATHS Matters 1999
Early Number Kit ISBN 186509 210X
Exploring 6 – 10
ISBN-13: 978 186509 212 6
ISBN-10: 186509 212 6

Reprinted 2006, 2007

Published by Blake Education
Locked Bag 2022
Glebe NSW 2037
www.blake.com.au

Printed by Green Giant Press
Illustration and design by Janice Bowles

Contents

How to use the activities

Each number from 6-10, including 0, is explored as a separate unit with 20 or more suggested activities and blackline masters.

The overall objective is to develop knowledge, skills and understandings for the numbers 6-10 in a variety of fun, child-centred ways.

The overall outcome for each unit is to estimate, count, compare, order and represent whole numbers up to 10.

A complete list of Outcome Indicators is provided on p.91 to help you see how and when this objective has been reached.

Each activity includes coded specific Outcome Indicators to help your planning, programming and unit assessment.

This example shows how easy it is to use each activity in your classroom.

Grouping strategies

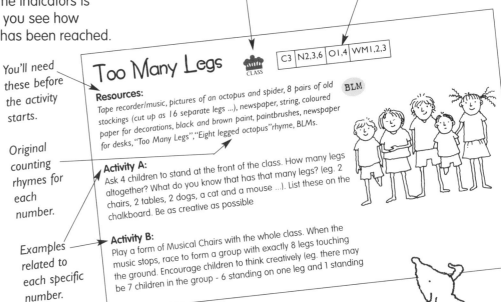

ONE = individual

PAIR = pair

GROUP = small group

CLASS = whole class

Coded Outcome Indicators
(see p. 91)

S = Sorting
N = Numeration
P = Patterning
C = Counting
O = Operations
WM = Working Mathematically

You'll need these before the activity starts.

Original counting rhymes for each number.

Examples related to each specific number.

Too Many Legs

CLASS

C3 | N2,3,6 | O1,4 | WM1,2,3

BLM

Resources:
Tape recorder/music, pictures of an octopus and spider, 8 pairs of old stockings (cut up as 16 separate legs ...), newspaper, string, coloured paper for decorations, black and brown paint, paintbrushes, newspaper for desks, "Too Many Legs", "Eight legged octopus" rhyme, BLMs.

Activity A:
Ask 4 children to stand at the front of the class. How many legs altogether? What do you know that has that many legs? (eg. 2 chairs, 2 tables, 2 dogs, a cat and a mouse ...). List these on the chalkboard. Be as creative as possible

Activity B:
Play a form of Musical Chairs with the whole class. When the music stops, race to form a group with exactly 8 legs touching the ground. Encourage children to think creatively (eg. there may be 7 children in the group - 6 standing on one leg and 1 standing

How to use the sample programs

A special feature of this book is the Sample Yearly Program for Mathematics (see p.92).

This shows one way to organise a 40 week teaching year for 5 year olds, exploring each number for a week at a time, as well as fitting in explorations in Space, Measurement, Chance and Data.
Another feature is the Sample Weekly Program for Mathematics (see p.93 for complete details). This shows you one way to organise a a selection of activities from "Exploring 7" (see p.20-34) as a five day unit, using the activities with the whole class, groups, pairs and/or individuals.

- A general example of a Weekly Program is available in Book 1 : Exploring 1-5 (p.91) showing how you could manage rotating groups over a five day period.
- A blank Weekly Program Proforma is also available in Book 1 : Exploring 1-5 (p.93). Use this to write your own weekly program based on the example shown here.

Sample Weekly Program

STRAND Number
GRADE K

SUBSTRAND Numeration (Exploring 7)
TERM 2   WEEK 5

OUTCOMES
- sorts/draws objects into groups of 7
- puts groups of 1 - 7 objects into counting order
- matches numerals to groups of 7 objects
- puts numeral cards 1-7 into counting order
- states the number of objects in groups up to 7
- states the order of an object from 1st to 7th

LANGUAGE
- "more than ...", "fewer than ..."
- "the same number as ..."
- "as many as ", "not enough"
- "there's ... altogether in this group"
- "this one has the smallest number of objects in it"

RESOURCES
"Snow White" book
numeral cards 1-7
1st to 7th cards
1-7 spinners

paint in 7 rainbow colours
brushes
0-7 dot cards
paper bags

building bricks:
(DUPLO, multilink, cuisenaire rods ...)
gold bottle tops

playdough
cookie cutters
BLM photocopies
scissors, crayons

MONDAY	TUESDAY	WEDNESDAY	THURSDAY	FRIDAY
• Read "Snow White". Discuss/role play Snow White and the 7 Dwarfs	• General discussion of rainbows and 7 colours	• "What day is it?"	• Rotating Group Activities (5 minutes)	• "The Dwarfs' Challenge"
• Discuss numeral for 7. Write in air. Sort 1-7 cards into order.	• Rotating Group Activities (10 minutes)	• "Weekly Jobs for Dwarfs"	"What a lot of stairs"	• Free activities related to 7
• Discuss "7th". Sort 1st to 7th cards into order.	"Colour a rainbow"	• "Snow White's Week"	"What a lot of bricks"	(eg. Design your own jewellery, How Hairy, Press and Guess, 7 letter words, 7-sided shapes on geoboards, drawing 7-pointed stars ...)
• Role play number rhyme "7 Dwarfs"	"Rainbow Dwarfs"	• How many fingers? Finish with fast whole class game using random numeral cards. Children hold up fingers to match	"Mining for gold"	
	• How many dots? Finish with fast whole class estimation game using random dot cards.		"Snow White's cookies"	
			• How many in a Huggle? Finish with fast whole class game using random numeral cards (huggles) to match.	• Role play number rhyme "7 Dwarfs"

6	●●● ●●●	six
7	●●● ●● ●● ●●	seven
8	●●● ● ●●● ●	eight
9	● ●●● ● ●●●	nine
0		zero

6th	sixth
7th	seventh
8th	eighth
9th	ninth
10th	tenth

Exploring

6

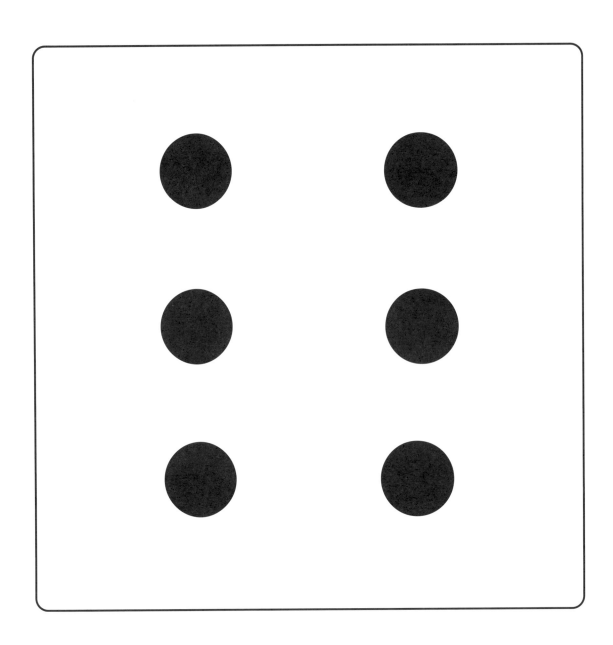

Exploring 6 – 10 **6** *Blake Education Reproducible*

Six green grasshoppers

Six green grasshoppers munch without a care.
Six pretty butterflies flutter through the air.
Six hungry cockroaches come out at night.
Six soldier ants rear up ready to fight.
Six bright blue dragonflies dart to the sky.
Six bright red beetles crawl slowly by.

Beetles and butterflies, bugs, flies and bees,
They all have six legs and six knobbly knees.

1 2 3   4 5 6

What does it say?

 CLASS

Resources:
A calculator for each child, paper strips, pencils.

Activity A:
Warm up. Ask 6 children to call out a number from 1-6 in turn.
Everyone presses these in to his/her calculator.
eg. "2", "5", "4", "1" , "3", "3"
Once the sixth number has been entered,
show your calculator display to your partner.
What does it say? (*254133*)
Does everyone have the same display?

Activity B:
PAIR
Work with a partner.
Press in ①⊕⊕ then press ⊜ six times.
Show your calculator to your partner.
Do you both have the same number?
If not, press ⓒ and start again.
If you both have the same number (*6*),
write this at the top of your paper strip,
then press ⊜ six more times.
What does the display show now? (*12*)
Write this new number under the first.
Continue pressing ⊜ six times
and recording the number shown.

What's the largest number any pair can get to ?

Russian Dolls

 CLASS

Resources:
A set of 6 nested Russian Dolls, "Russian Dolls" BLM, **BLM**
scissors, paste, workbook.

Activity A:
Who has 6 children in their family?
Do you know anyone like this?
Select 6 children to come to the front
who are different heights. Count them.
How can we put these people into order
from the tallest to the shortest? (Sort)

Show the nested Russian Dolls. Discuss.
Open up to reveal each one. Count them.
Ask children to bring in other examples
of nested wooden toys from home.

Children colour then cut out the paper dolls
and paste them into size order in their workbooks.
Show me the first doll, the second ... the last one.
Which one is the middle-size doll? How do you know?

Russian Dolls

How many bounces? | C3 | N2 | O3 | WM2,3 |

Resources:

Large balls (enough for 1 ball between 2 at the most ...).

Activity:

How many times do you think this ball will bounce
if I drop it from up here? (eg. stand up on a chair ...)
Guess first, drop the ball and count the number of bounces.
Do any balls bounce six times or more?

CLASS

Work with a partner. Can you throw and catch the ball 6 times
without dropping it?
Can you bounce the ball along the ground 6 times without stopping?

PAIR

Count the dots | C3 | N1,2 | O1 | WM2 |

Resources:

*A set of dominoes, 3 empty containers (eg. margarine ...)
for each group of 6 children.*

Activity:

Turn the dominoes all face down.
On a given signal, race to turn them face up
and sort them into 3 containers as follows:

GROUP

> -more than 6 dots
> -exactly 6 dots
> -fewer than 6 dots

Which team is the fastest? How can you check your sorting?

Build the Butterflies | GROUP | N3,4 | WM2 |

Resources:

Butterfly poster, "Build the Butterflies" BLM, felt pens, scissors. **BLM**

Activity:

Discuss the poster. How many legs does a butterfly have?
(Butterflies are insects so they all have 6 legs ...)

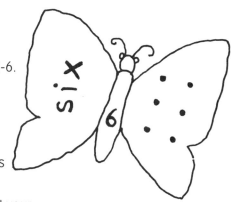

Children work in groups of 6. They decide on a number each from 1-6.
Each person writes their number word on the left wing, draws the
number of dots on the right wing and writes their numeral on the
butterfly's body.

Colour in each butterfly. Cut out as an A5 card with the butterfly's
body and legs and the 2 wings cut out separately. Place the 2 wings
on top of the body to construct a complete butterfly.

Jumble up all the pieces in the middle of your group. Try to construct your
butterfly again by matching the number name and dots wings to the butterfly
body showing the matching numeral. Ask a friend to check your matching.

Build the Butterflies

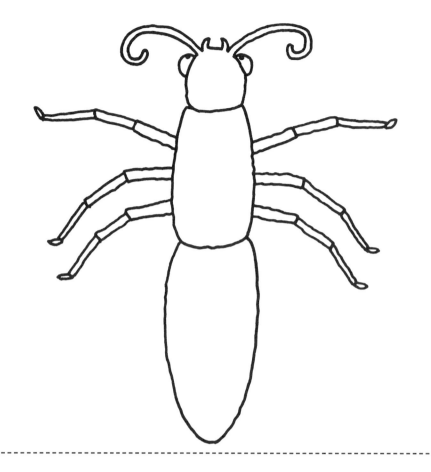

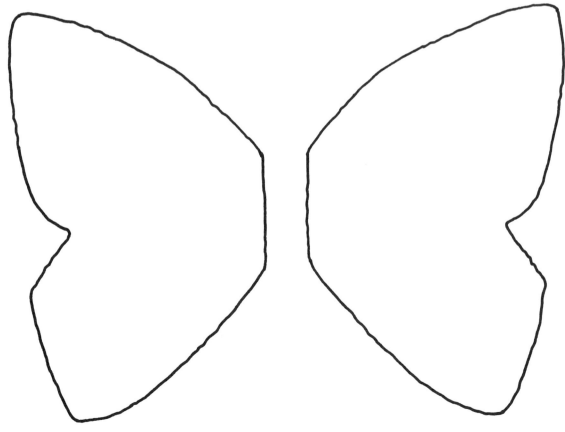

Hexagons

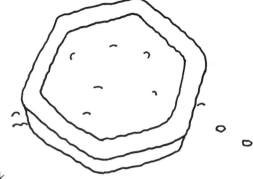

Resources:
Hexagonal-shaped biscuits, hexagonal polydrons,
wooden/plastic hexagons.

Activity:
Ask everyone to close their eyes. Pass around the wooden/plastic
shapes. Ask the children to feel them and try to visualise
what the shape will look like once they open their eyes.
Discuss (while everyone still has their eyes shut).

Open your eyes. Were you close? What can we call this shape? (Look
for a variety of answers . . .) What is so special about this shape? (Look for
creative responses). It has 6 straight sides and 6 corners. It is a hexagon.
Each child takes a biscuit and compares shapes with a partner. Finish by eating
the biscuits!

Draw a Hexagon

Resources:
Wooden/plastic hexagons, crayons/pencils, paper.

Activity A:
Hand out hexagonal shapes. Feel, discuss. Can you draw a hexagon? Ask
some children to come to the front to demonstrate. Practise drawing in the air
as large as you can. What do you notice? (eg. the opposite sides go in the same
direction ...). Children trace their hexagonal shapes onto paper and decorate.

Activity B:
Do all the sides have to be equal? Try drawing hexagons on paper so that the
sides are different lengths and the shapes are quite irregular. Can you make a
pattern from these hexagons?

Draw a star

Resources:
Wooden/plastic hexagons, crayons/pencils, paper.

Activity:
Draw a large, regular hexagon on the chalkboard.
Tell the children that there are even more special things about this shape. What
will happen if you continue drawing the lines to make outer triangles?
(Guess first, then demonstrate) When you have finished, count up the number of
small triangles. There are 6 altogether!

Can anyone see any other patterns? A 6-pointed star looks like 2 triangles on
top of one another. Can you see them? This is another way you can draw the
star (demonstrate). Children trace or draw their own hexagon on paper and turn
this into a 6-pointed star. Explain to a friend how to draw a star your way.

Jellyfish

 CLASS | C4 | N3 | O1 | WM3 | S4 |

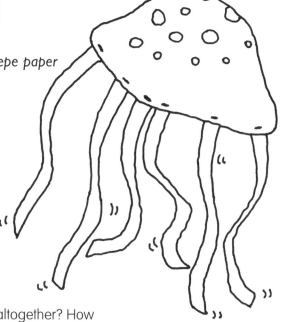

Resources:
Poster of a jellyfish (or a book about jellyfish ...), cardboard, crepe paper streamers, scissors, paste.

Activity:
Discuss jellyfish. Has anyone seen one in real life? What do they look like? What do they feel like?

Imagine that each jellyfish has 6 tentacles. Demonstrate how to make your own jellyfish by drawing a jellyfish body and cutting this out.

Next tear off 6 paper streamers and paste these to the base of the cutout.

Display around the room in clusters of 6. How many jellyfish altogether? How many tentacles?
What are 6 more things you would like to know about jellyfish?

Lots of Legs

| C4 | S1,2,3 | N3 | P1 | WM3 |

Resources:
Posters, books about insects, a large plastic model of an insect, small plastic insect counters, copy of "Six Green Grasshoppers ..." number rhyme (p. 10).

Activity:
What is an insect? Can you name some?
(List or draw on the board ...)

 CLASS

ants	grasshoppers
bees	flies
beetles	butterflies
moths	cockroaches
dragonfly	mosquitoes
"bugs"	

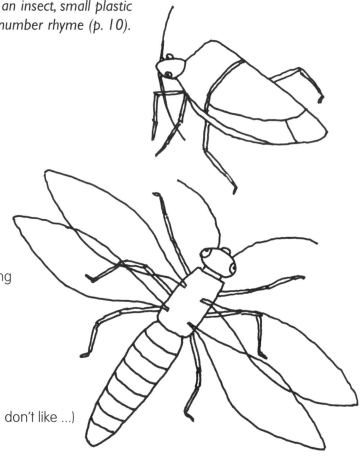

What is the same about all of these creatures?
(eg. 3 parts to their body, 6 legs ...). Recite the counting rhyme together.

Children work in groups to investigate the small plastic insects.
Can they identify the heads? GROUP
The middle parts? (thorax)
The lower body part? (the abdomen)
How could you sort your insects? (eg. the ones I like, don't like ...)

Written Activity:
Draw your insect. Try to make it as realistic as possible. Make sure you show the 6 legs!

Draw a 6 [C1] [N4]

Resources:
*Shaving cream, kitchen cloths
(for wiping up each desk at the end of the activity ...),
numeral and word cards for 1-6.*

Activity:
Discuss the shape of the numeral "6".
Discuss what it reminds the children of in real life.
eg.   "a cherry", "half a pair of glasses",
         "an Indian with a feather on the left ..."
Sort the cards into counting order forwards then backwards.

Demonstrate how to write a "6" starting from the top,
dragging down, curving out to the right then sweeping back
in a smooth motion. Practise tracing large 6s in the air, small 6s in the air.

Discuss the numeral cards. Trace over each shape with your finger,
starting at the top left and dragging down.

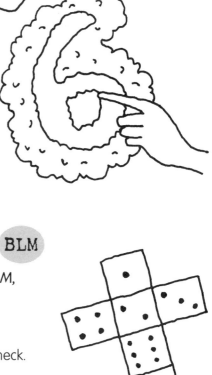

Written activity:
Spread a small amount of shaving cream on the children's desks.
Practise writing 6s by swirling your finger through the cream!

Make a cube [C3] [N3] [O1] [P1] GROUP   BLM

Resources:
*A large wooden/plastic cube, a cardboard box with a lid, "Make a cube" BLM,
scissors, paste.*

Activity:
Hold up a cube. How many faces does it have? Guess first then count to check.
How many corners? How many edges?

Discuss the cardboard box. What could we call this object? What can we do with it?
(eg. a box to put something in, a toy for a young child to play with, dice for a game ...)

Explain that everyone will be able to make their own cube. Demonstrate how to cut,
fold and paste the net to construct a cube. Demonstrate how to draw in dots from 1-6
to turn your cube into a die for a game. (If you follow the pattern shown here, when
the cube is folded you will have the opposite sides adding to 7).

Who has more? [C3,5] [N3] [O1] PAIR

Resources:
Home-made dice, counters.

Activity:
Work with a partner. Take turns to throw the die.
Whoever has the largest number wins a counter.
Try to be the first to get exactly 6 counters.

Make a cube

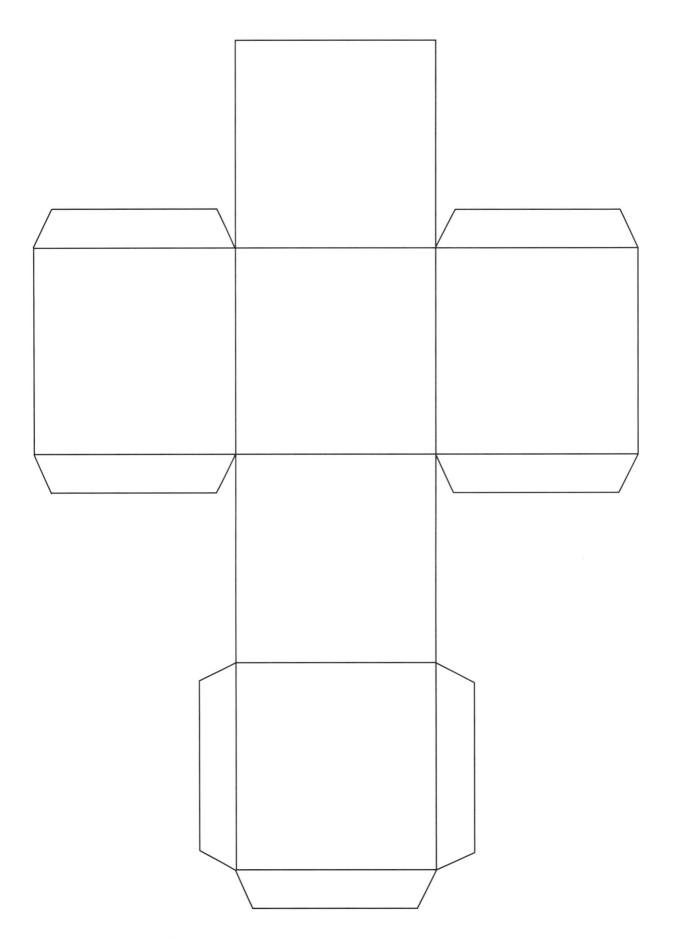

Buzz off

 GROUP | C1,3 | N3 | WM2

Resources:
One die, 3 bee counters (photocopy the 3 bees shown here, colour, laminate, cut out), "Buzz off" BLM photocopied to A3 for every 3 children.

BLM

Activity:
Work in groups of 3. Take turns to throw the die and move your "Bee" along the flower trail the number of spaces shown on the die. Try to be the first bee to reach the beehive.

How many groups of 6 flowers did you cross?
How many flowers in one line?

Spin to win

 GROUP | S4 | N1,2,3,4 | WM2,3

Resources:
Dots/numerals "Spinners 1-6" BLM, stiff cardboard, scissors, paste, short skewers, a large pile of building blocks (eg. DUPLO, multilink ...) for each group of 4 children.

BLM

Activity A:
Photocopy the spinners onto brightly coloured paper.

Each child pastes one spinner onto some stiff cardboard, then cuts this out.

Insert a short skewer through the centre.

Practise twirling the spinner and identifying the number that it lands on. Check for bias.

Activity B:
Sit in groups of 4 with a spinner and a pile of building bricks in the centre of the group.

Take turns to spin the spinner and take that many bricks.

Stop the group after 6 minutes.
Who has the most bricks?
Who can build the tallest tower?
How do you know it is the tallest?
(eg. match the heights of each tower ...)

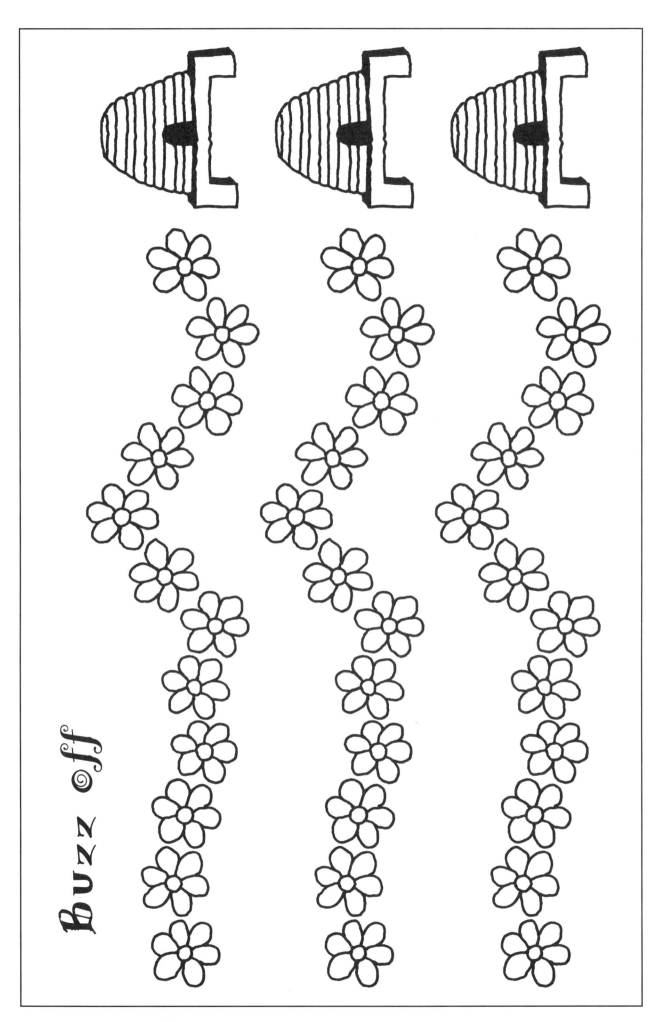

Buzz off

Spinners 1 – 6

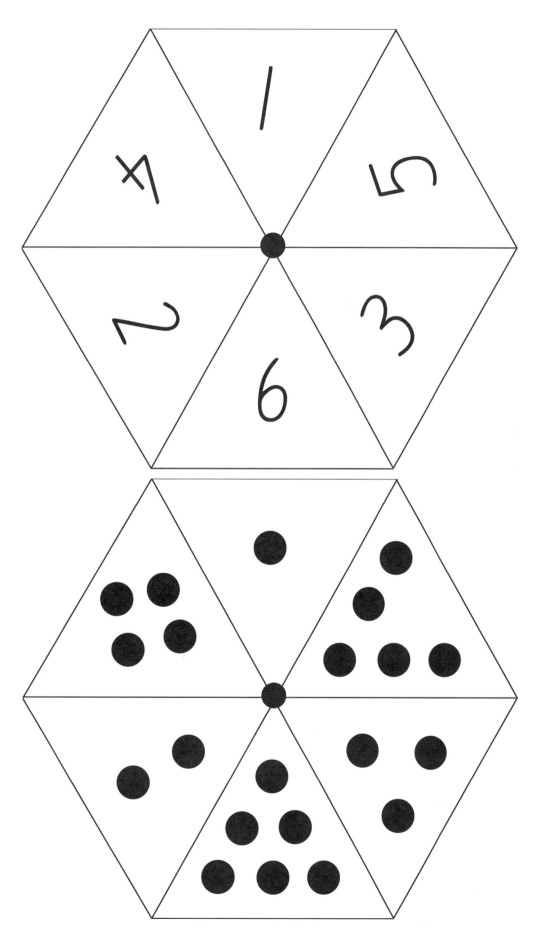

Exploring 7

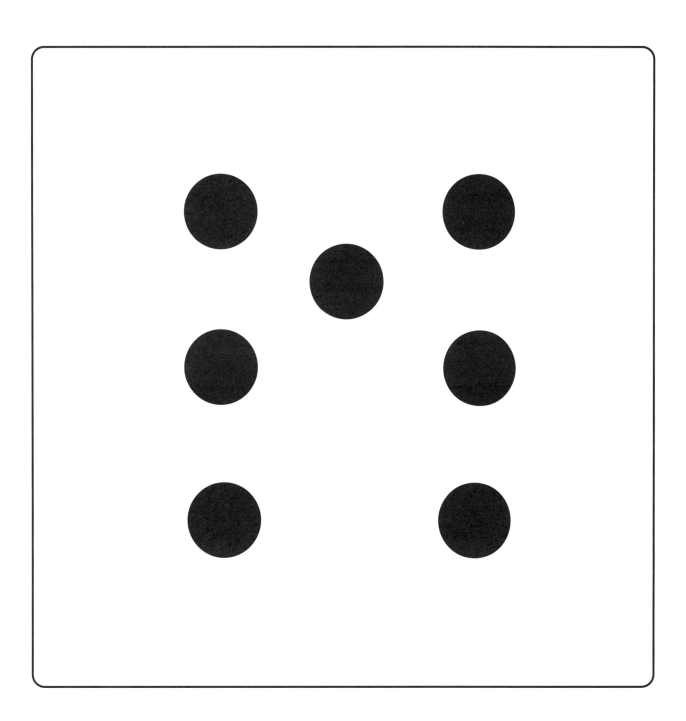

seven

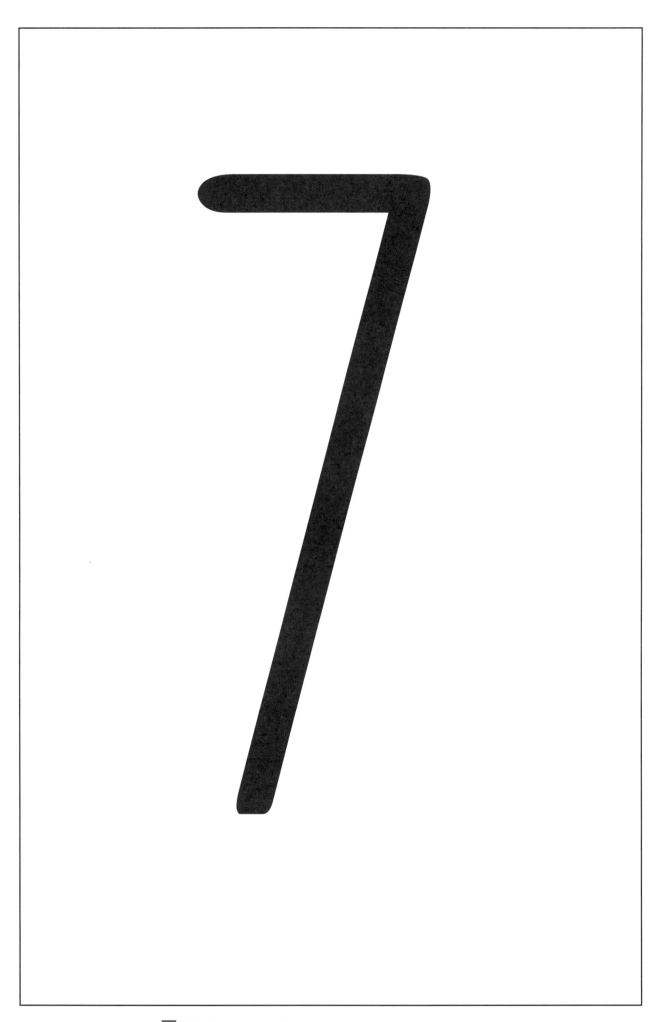

The Seven Dwarfs

Seven little dwarfs went out one day,
Over the hills and far away.
When it was time for them all to come home,
Snow White took out her mobile phone.
She politely said "Please take to the track."
But when they reached home only six had come back!

(Repeat, subtracting one dwarf each time until ...
"But when she looked out not one dwarf had
come back!")

Poor Snow White didn't know what to do,
Without her seven friends she felt lonely and blue.
"I know" said Snow White, "I'll walk there myself".
So she took down her backpack from off the shelf.
And when at last she reached the mine,
There were the seven dwarfs standing in line!

1 2 3 4 5 6 7

Snow White

| S1,2,4 | C1,2,3 | N3,5 | O1,2 | WM1,2,3 |

Resources:

Snow White picture/story book, (preferably based on the original Grimmsversion), numeral/ number word cards 1-7, ordinal cards "1st" to "7th"/"first" to "seventh" for each group of 7 children, "The Seven Dwarfs" rhyme (p.23).

Activity A:

Recall/discuss the story. Ask 7 children to come to the front and hold up a number card each. Select another child to be Snow White. The dwarfs try to trick her by mixing themselves up.

Snow White has to rearrange them so that they are back in counting order from 1 to 7. Can they be sorted from 7 to 1 counting backwards?

Activity B:

Children, in groups of 7 dwarfs, take a 1-7 position card at random eg. "Seventh". Can they now rearrange themselves into counting order?

Activity C:

Children, in groups of 7 dwarfs, sort themselves into order from the tallest to the shortest. Extra children walk round asking questions related to positions. eg. Which dwarf is after the third dwarf? Who is the last dwarf? Is the sixth dwarf shorter than the fourth dwarf?

Activity D:

Act out the number rhyme "The Seven Dwarfs". Make up your own verses too! Practise counting backwards from 7 to 0.

Colour a Rainbow

 CLASS GROUP | S1,2 | N5 | P1,3 | WM3 |

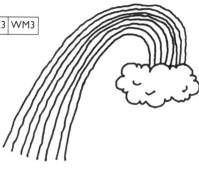

Resources:
Red, orange, yellow, green, blue, dark blue (indigo -the colour of night), purple/violet paint, paper, brushes, poster or book about rainbows.

Activity A:
Discuss the rainbow poster. Talk about the 7 basic colours in every rainbow, starting with red and finishing with violet (R O Y G B I V) These colours always appear in the same order, like magic. Demonstrate how to paint a rainbow by placing the paint in the same order as the poster.

Cover your paper with rainbow stripes. Ask each other questions related to position (eg. Which colour is fifth?)

Activity B:
Practise painting 7s in rainbow colours on paper.

Rainbow Dwarfs

| S1,2 | N1,2,3,5,6 | P1,2 | WM1,2 | C3 |

Resources:
"The Seven Dwarfs" BLM, crayons in 7 rainbow colours, scissors.    BLM

Activity A:
Colour each dwarf a separate colour, cut out, mix up then arrange the dwarfs into rainbow order.

ONE

Activity B:
Arrange some of the dwarfs in a new order. Tell a partner about this (eg. The red one is not last. The yellow one is first.) How many other combinations follow these clues?

PAIR

Activity C:
Take some dwarfs each at random. Guess how many you have, how many your partner has. How many have not been used this time? Who has more dwarfs? Fewer? The same number? Repeat several times. Do your guesses get closer? Do you have an odd or an even number of dwarfs?

The Seven Dwarfs

What day is it?

| S1 | N4 | P1 | WM2,3 |

 GROUP

Resources:
"What day is it?" BLM, scissors. BLM

Activity:
Revise the days of the week. How many days altogether? What do you know that is special about each day? How do we know when it's the weekend? (eg. we don't go to school on Sunday...). Discuss suggestions together.

Discuss days of the week using the namecards. Sort into order. What is the second day of the week? The last? Which day is Sunday? (the first day ...) Which day comes next?
Ask children to invent their own questions for the class to answer.

Weekly Jobs for Dwarfs

| S2 | N3 | O3 | WM3 |

Resources:
"What day is it?" BLM, large paper, feltpens. BLM CLASS

Activity:
Make a list of 7 things Snow White could ask the dwarfs to do over a week. (eg. Monday "Make your bed", Tuesday "Wash your socks", Wednesday "Take your boots off before you come inside"...). Encourage the children to respond creatively. Write each task in a different colour.

Written Activity:
Children record days in order by copying them into a workbook. They then create their own Weekly Jobs List using pictures or words.

Snow White's Week

| O3 | WM3 |

 CLASS

Resources:
"What day is it?" BLM. BLM

 GROUP

Activity:
Revise the story of Snow White making the actions happen over one week. What might happen on Monday? On which day did the Queen give Snow White the apple? When did the prince arrive? (Individual children suggest questions to discuss.)

What day is it?

Sunday

Monday

Tuesday

Wednesday

Thursday

Friday

Saturday

What a lot of stairs | S1,2,3 | C3 | N3,5 | O3 | WM2 |

Resources:
A pile of unifix/multilink blocks/DUPLO 4-stud bricks/cuisenaire rods for each group, paper, crayons.

Activity:
Imagine the 7 dwarfs had 7 stairs leading up to their front door. What might these look like? Work together to build a set of 7 stairs for the dwarfs. Make each stair a different colour. Ask each other questions, related to position. (eg. Is the third stair yellow? What colour is the first stair?) Draw a picture of your stairs with a dwarf standing on each one.

What a lot of bricks | C3 | N3 | O1 | WM2 |

Resources:
Unifix, multilink blocks, DUPLO 4-stud bricks, 1-7 numeral cards.

Activity:
Place the cards face down in the centre. Take turns to turn over a card and collect the corresponding number of bricks. After everyone has had 3 turns, stop and count how many bricks each person has collected. Guess first then check. Can anyone count how many bricks altogether? Work co-operatively. Combine all the bricks to build a house for the dwarfs.

Mining for Gold | C1,3 | N2,3 | O1 | WM1,2 |

Resources:
Gold bottle tops, paper bag, "Spinners 1-7" BLM (dot or numerals, with short skewer through the centre) for each group.

BLM

Activity:
The 7 dwarfs are working in a gold mine this week. Take turns to twirl the spinner to see how much gold you collect with each dig. Put the corresponding number of gold nuggets into your bag. Guess how much gold you have collected after 7 spins. How can you check your guess? How many groups of 7 nuggets are there?

Snow White's Cookies | C3 | N1,3 | O1,3 | S1,2,4 |

Resources:
Playdough in 7 colours, cookie cutters, newspaper on desks, small numeral cards 1-7.

 GROUP

Activity:
Children make groups of 7 cookies for the dwarfs, either all in one colour or in 7 different colours. How many cookies altogether? Place the numeral cards face down in the centre of the group. Turn over a card. Race to collect that many cookies. Guess how many cookies collected altogether each time. Check by counting.

Spinners 1 – 7

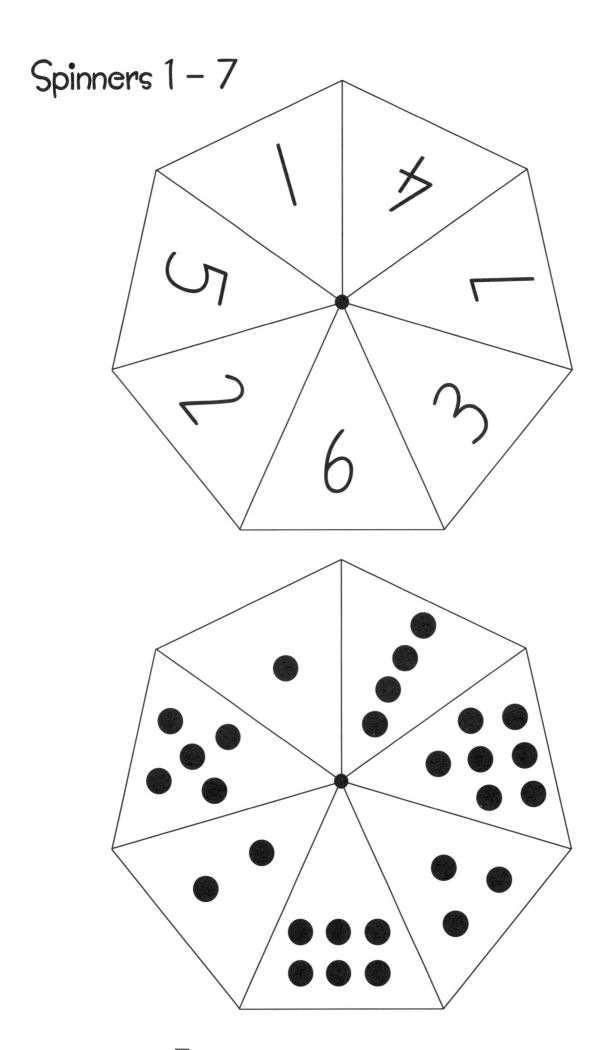

The Dwarfs' Challenge

Resources:
*"The Dwarfs' Challenge" BLM (for each child), scissors, "Make a 7",
"What is this?" BLMs, a large cardboard tangram, bluetac, pencil/paper.*

 BLM

Activity A:
The dwarfs like to challenge themselves with puzzles. Here is one of their favourite ones. How many pieces are there? (Start with the large tangram stuck in the shape of a square to the chalkboard. Ask 7 children to come to the front and take a piece each). Can you rearrange the pieces to make the dwarf's square again? (This is a very difficult task. Don't worry if they can't remake it ...).

What can you make? Try rearranging the pieces on the board one at a time (making any shape ...). Discuss the fact that there are always 7 pieces no matter how many times you rearrange them. What does it remind you of? Why? Can you make the shapes look like a bird? A human?

Activity B:
Demonstrate how to rearrange the 7 pieces to construct the shape shown on "Make a 7". Children cut out their individual tangrams and match the pieces to make the 7. Discuss the clue lines and how some pieces may need to be turned over or around. Fast workers can rearrange their pieces to make a new shape.

 ONE

Activity C:
Cut out the 4 cards shown on "What is this?" Discuss what each of the pictures reminds everyone of in real life. What clues are there to help you put the 7 pieces back together?

 GROUP

Fast workers can create their own picture for a friend to copy by tracing around the edges of each piece in their picture. You could then reduce this on the photocopier. Build up a class collection of pictures to copy.

Make it Seven

 CLASS 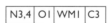 N3,4 | O1 | WM1 | C3

Resources:
Paper, crayons/pencils.

Activity:
Everyone writes the numerals 1 to 7 down the page in order. Draw pictures beside each number to show how many altogether. Some children may like to continue the Snow White theme (eg, 7: Draw seven miner's hammers ...) Ask children to explain their selection to a friend. How many objects drawn altogether?

1
2
3
4
5
6
7

The Dwarf's Challenge

Make a 7

What is this?

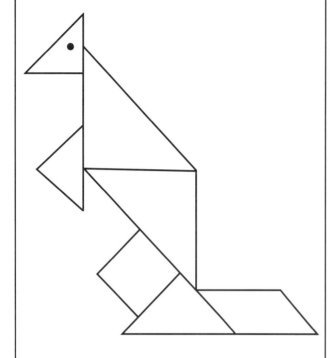

What is this?

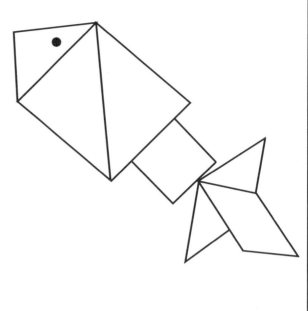

What is this?

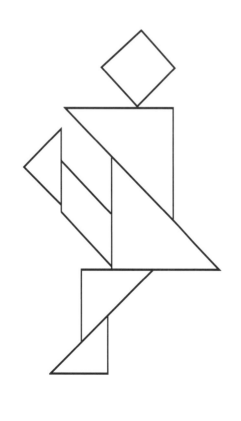

What is this?

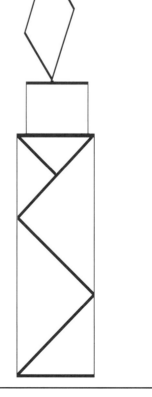

Exploring

8

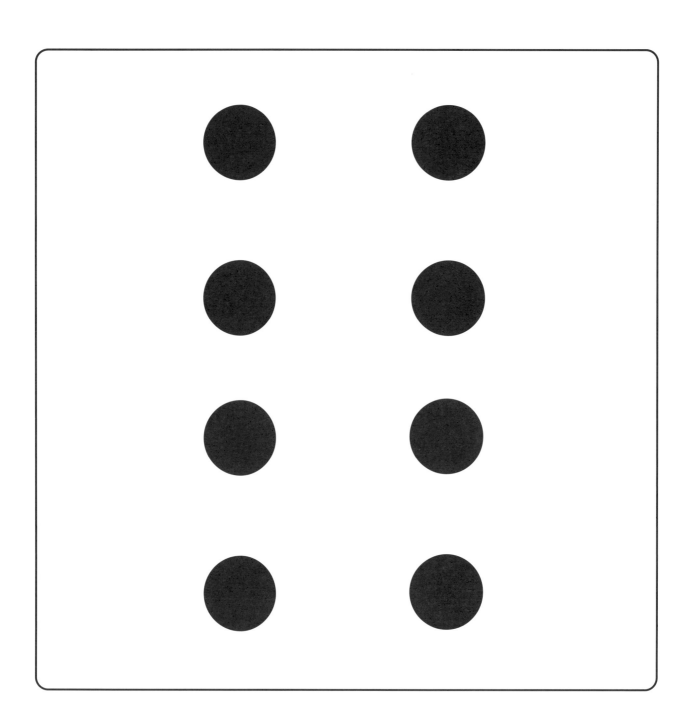

eight

Eight legged octopus

If I were an octopus out for the day
I'd call all my octopus friends here to play.

We'd slither and slide,
We'd glither and glide.
We'd burble and bubble
And cause so much trouble,
We'd frighten the fish all away.

Eight legs would tangle
Squash tightly and mangle.

Eight legs would quiver
And make the fish shiver.

Eight legs would bobble
And wiggle and wobble.

Eight legs would jiggle
And hold tight and wriggle.

Oh! If I were an octopus out for the day
I'd count up the legs then swim
out round the bay.

1, 2, 3, 4, 5, 6, 7, 8 ...

Race Track

Resources:

"8" BLM as an overhead transparency, overhead projector, containers of water/large brushes, chalk, stopwatch (optional).

BLM

Activity A:

Discuss the "8" overhead. What does it remind you of in real life? (eg. 2 doughnuts, a racing track...) Trace over the 8, demonstrating how to start at the top right (about 2 o'clock on a clockface ...) then drawing down in an anti-clockwise direction. Everyone practises drawing large 8s in the air, making racetrack noises as you go!

CLASS

Activity B:

Go out into playground. Practise painting huge racetrack 8s on the ground with water and large brushes. Who can make the largest?

Activity C:

Divide the class into teams of 8 children. Draw a gigantic 8 with chalk in front of each team. Explain how these are the tracks for the team races. Explain how to run along the track the same way you write an 8 on paper. The first person from each team lines up at the start. On a signal, each runner races along the track, returns to the start and touches the second player, who commences running. The winning team is the first one to have all 8 runners back to the start.

GROUP

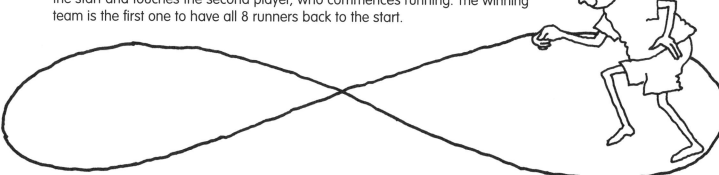

Match them up

GROUP

BLM

Resources:

"Match them up"BLM, number word cards "one" to "eight", feltpens, scissors, an envelope for each team.

Activity:

Discuss "eight" (the number name for 8). Revise, sort the word cards "one" to "seven" too, forwards and backwards.

Children work in teams of 8. Each person is allocated a number from 1 to 8. (Exra children need 8 photocopies between them). Each person writes/copies his/her number name on the racing car body. They write the numeral on the left wheel and draw in the matching number of dots/ spokes on the right wheel. Ask children to check each other's work before continuing.

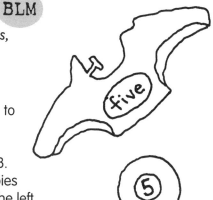

Colour in, then cut out each racing car as three separate pieces. Store in an envelope.

Each team mixes up all their pieces then passes their envelope to the next team. Teams then try to resort all the pieces so that the racing car parts all match.

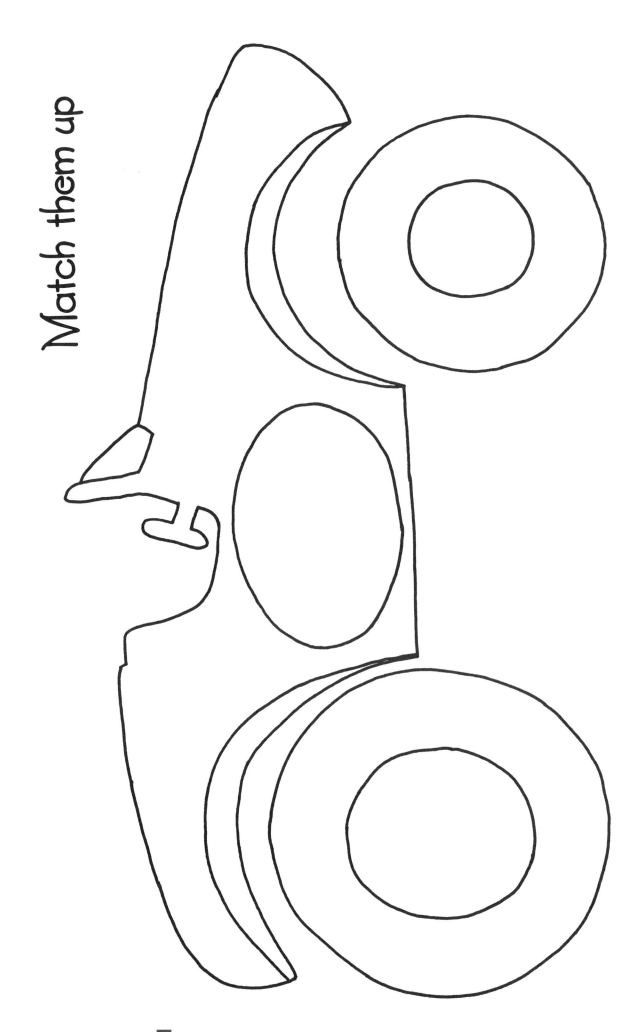

Match them up

Too Many Legs

S1,2,3 | N1,3,4 | O1,3 | P1 | WM1,2,3

Resources:

Tape recorder/music, pictures of an octopus and spider, 8 pairs of old stockings (cut up as 16 separate legs ...), newspaper, string, coloured paper for decorations, black and brown paint, paintbrushes, newspaper for desks, "Too Many Legs", "Eight legged octopus" rhyme, BLMs.

BLM

Activity A:

CLASS

Ask 4 children to stand at the front of the class. How many legs altogether? What do you know that has that many legs? (eg. 2 chairs, 2 tables, 2 dogs, a cat and a mouse ...). List these on the chalkboard. Be as creative as possible.

Activity B:

Play a form of Musical Chairs with the whole class. When the music stops, race to form a group with exactly 8 legs touching the ground. Encourage children to think creatively (eg. there may be 7 children in the group - 6 standing on one leg and 1 standing on 2 legs ...). Anyone left out has to sit down.

Activity C:

Ask the children to think of a creature that has exactly 8 legs (eg, a spider, an octopus ...). Discuss the pictures of a spider and octopus. Discuss feelings and personal reactions/stories about each of these creatures. List 8 words on the board which describe the children's feelings towards each of these creatures (eg. Spider: scary, clever ...)

Activity D:

GROUP

Divide the children into 8 groups. Four groups will each make 2 legs of a spider model, the other four groups will each make 2 legs of an octopus model. Scrunch up sheets of newspaper and stuff them into the leg of a stocking. Work co-operatively to construct the large model. Hang finished models in the classroom.

Activity E:

ONE

Fast workers can cut out/ paste or draw their own pictures of a large octopus and a spider. How many legs altogether? Guess first, then check. What if there were 3 spiders? How many legs then? What if there was a spider and 2 octopuses? Encourage the class to invent their own stories/problems about legs.

Activity F:

Read the Counting Rhyme (p.38).
Act out using octopus models.

CLASS

Too Many Legs

Too Many Legs

How many sides?

 CLASS | S1,2 | C4 | N3 | WM1,2,3

Resources:

An outline of a large octagon on the chalkboard covered by a sheet of newspaper, a variety of octagons, a picture/photo of a stopsign (or take the children to see a real one close to the school ...).

Activity A:

Remove the newspaper to reveal the octagon on the chalkboard. Ask the children to look at it silently for one minute, then close their eyes. Cover the shape up again.

The children open their eyes and tell you what they saw (eg. it was drawn in yellow chalk ...). Have they seen this shape before? How many sides do they think it had? Have they ever seen a shape like this in real life? Close to the school?
Reveal the shape again. Count the number of sides. Explain that the special name for this shape is an octagon. Ask someone to draw an octagon on the board. Everyone tries to draw an octagon in the air.

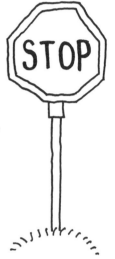

Activity B:

If possible, walk outside and look at a real stop sign. Ask the children to suggest reasons for why this sign is that shape, that colour ... (This red octagon is used all over the world to tell vehicles to stop before moving through the intersection. It is a safety sign). Ask them to count how many stop signs they see in the next few days. Remember to check the numbers later in the week.

Activity C:

Pass around the mixed octagon shapes. Feel the sides. Count the corners. Draw or trace one of these shapes onto paper. How can you turn this shape into an 8-pointed star? Or an 8-petaled flower? Encourage different solution strategies.

Throw and Catch

  PAIR | C3 | N3

Resources:

A large ball for each pair of children.

Activity:

Take 8 steps away from your partner. Stop. Throw the ball. Can your partner catch it without dropping it? Can you throw and catch the ball 8 times without a break? If so, walk another 8 steps. Can you and your partner throw and catch the ball 8 times now?

Twirl it

 GROUP | C3 | N3 | WM3

Resources:

A hula hoop for each child.

Activity:

Can you twirl the hula hoop around your arm 8 times? Can you twirl it around your waist 8 times? Can you twirl it around your ankle held up high? Can you bowl your hoop and make it stay upright for 8 pushes? What else can you do?

Hopscotch

 GROUP | S4 | N3,4 | WM3 |

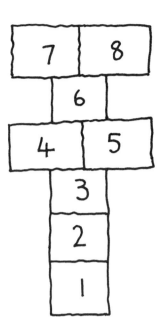

Resources:
Chalk, a pebble/token for each player.

Activity:
Draw a hopscotch grid on the playground with chalk. Explain the rules of the game. Throw your token onto "1". Hop onto each number from 2 to 8 and back again. Collect the token before starting again. This time throw to "2". Repeat until you have taken your token from 8.
Who can think of another game using this grid?

Up to eight

 CLASS | C5 | N3,4 | O1,3 | WM1,2 |

Activity:
A whole class oral question and answer game.
Make up some addition stories about numbers up to 8.
Ask the children to predict the answers.

eg. "Sam has 5 fish. He wants to have 8 fish altogether. How many more fish should he buy?"
"Vinh has $6. Her mum gives her another $2. How much money does she have now?"

Encourage individual children to invent their own story problems to ask the class. Encourage all children to explain the strategies they used to solve the problems.

Written Activity:
Some children may like to record their solutions on paper.

Down from eight

 CLASS | N3,4 | O2,3 | WM1,2 |

Activity:
A whole class oral question and answer game.
Make up some subtraction stories about numbers up to 8.
Ask the children to predict the answers.

eg. "I have 8 caterpillars. Three crawl away. How many do I have left?"
"Six cars are in a race. Two crash. How many are still racing?"
"Maria has 4 swap cards. Her friend Sally has 7. How many more cards does Sally have?"

Encourage individual children to invent their own story problems to ask the class. Encourage all children to explain the strategies they used to solve the problems.

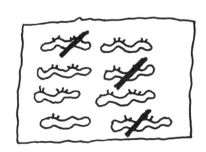

Written Activity:
Some children may like to record their solutions on paper.

Exploring

9

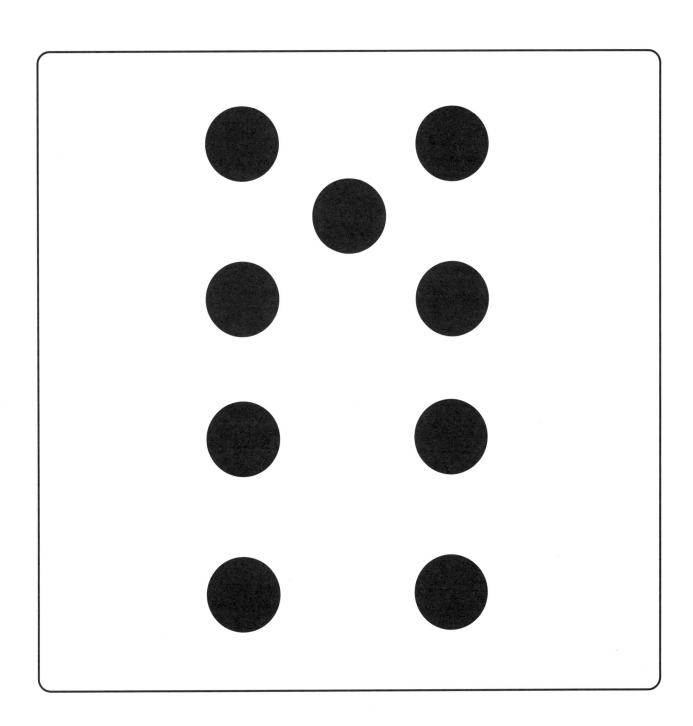

nine

Two wonderful witches

Two wonderful witches
Hitched up their britches
And decided to cast a big spell.
They needed nine hats
As well as nine bats
And nine furry black cats as well.

Together they mumbled,
Together they grumbled,
Then sorted the hats in two groups.
Together they wriggled
Together they jiggled
And their spell made everyone ... DROOP.

Together they mumbled,
Together they grumbled,
Then sorted the bats in two heaps.
Together they wriggled
Together they jiggled
And their spell made everyone ... SLEEP.

Together they mumbled,
Together they grumbled,
Then sorted the cats in two piles.
Together they wriggled
Together they jiggled
And their spell made everyone ... SMILE.

What's Missing?

S3 | N1,3 | O2 | WM1,2

Resources:
9 small objects, a 3 x 3 grid on an overhead, an overhead projector and screen.

Activity A:
Whole class activity. Place 9 small objects in the grid squares on the overhead screen. Discuss. Turn off the overhead and secretly remove one item. Turn the overhead on again. Can the children guess what's missing? Where was it? Encourage the use of position language (eg. "in the middle", "up in that corner..."). How many objects are there now? Repeat, removing up to all the objects in turn.

CLASS

Activity B:
Repeat this activity without the 3 x 3 grid. Place 9 small objects randomly on the screen.

GROUP

Activity C:
Repeat with children working in small groups, sitting in a circle. They collect 9 objects, place them in the centre of the group and elect a leader to remove the objects one by one. Play as for Activity A.

Who's in the square?

S1,2 | C3 | N3,4 | O1 | WM2

Resources:
Chalk, "What's in the square?" BLM. 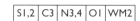 BLM

Activity:
Divide the class into groups of 9. In front of each group, draw a 3 x 3 grid (large enough to take a child in each square) with chalk on the playground. Label columns ▲ ● ■ . Label rows 1, 2, 3. Explain how to name each square (eg. "Triangle 1")

GROUP

Each child in the group stands on one square of the grid. Extra children stand with a friend in his/her square. Call out instructions for each team to follow eg. "Bob down if you are standing on Triangle 1." "Put your hands in the air and wave them around if you are standing on Circle 3."

Written Activity:
Children use a "What's in the square?" grid to design their own activity eg. a battleship-type game with a partner.

Join the dots

ONE · C1 | N3,4

Resources:
"Join the dots" BLM, crayons/pencils, tracing paper. BLM

Activity A:
Children join the dots from 1-9 to create the picture. How can you finish it off? (Join the 9 back to the 5). Colour.

Activity B:
Create your own "Join the dots" picture. Place tracing paper over a drawing and write the numbers 1-9 at key points.

What's in the square?

What's in the square?

Join the dots

Join the dots

Wonderful Witches

| S1,2 | C3 | N1,3,4 | O1,2,3, | WM1,2 | C5 |

Resources:
"Wonderful Witches", "Hats"/"Bats"/ "Cats" "Rhyme" BLMs, scissors, crayons, storage envelope (for each pair).

Activity A:
Colour and cut out the witches (as A5 cards). Colour and cut out the hats, bats or cats (as individual shapes). Store in envelopes or small plastic containers with lids.

PAIR

Activity B:
Discuss, role play the "Two wonderful witches" number rhyme for "9" (see p50). Use the cutouts to model some of the actions.

CLASS

Activity C:
Children work with a partner. Make up a story about the 9 hats. Sort the hats between the two witches and count up how many hats for each witch. Guess first then check.

PAIR

eg.

Place one witch's set of hats under the card. Can you guess how many are hidden just by looking at the other witch's hats?

Activity D:
Children work with a partner. Make up a story about the 9 bats. Sort the bats between the two witches and count up how many bats for each witch. Guess first then check.

PAIR

eg.

Close you eyes while your partner sorts the bats. Your partner tells you how many bats belong to one of the witches. Can you guess how many bats the other witch has just by thinking about it with your eyes shut? Take a guess then open your eyes and count.

Activity E:
Children work with a partner. Make up a story about the 9 cats. Sort the cats between the two witches and count up how many cats for each witch. Guess first then check.

PAIR

eg.

Find a way to record your discoveries on paper or in a workbook.

Wonderful Witches

Wonderful Witches

How many hats?

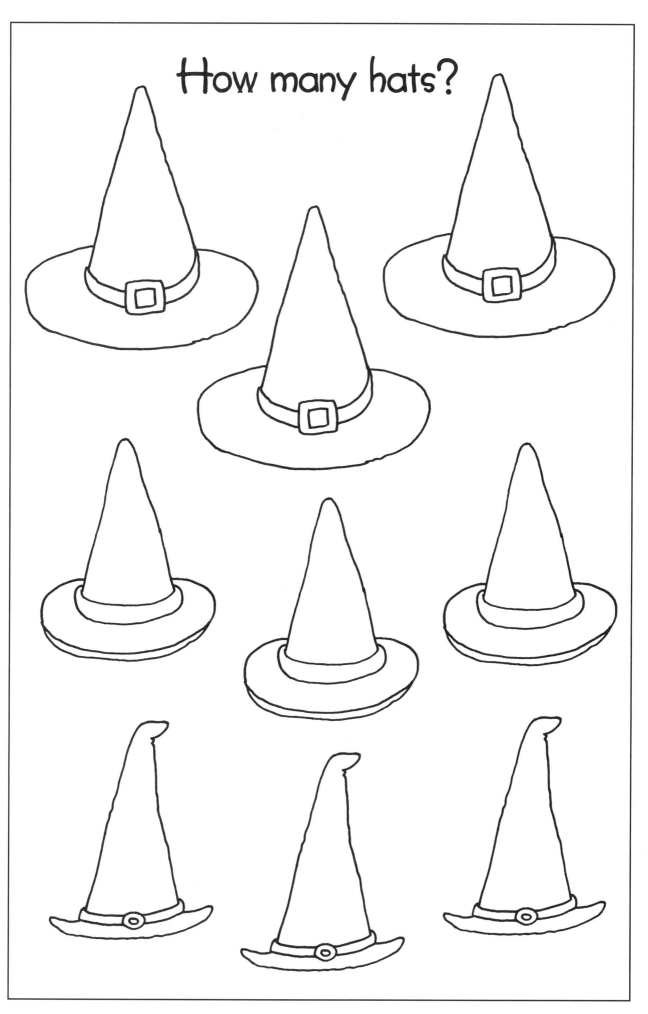

How many bats?

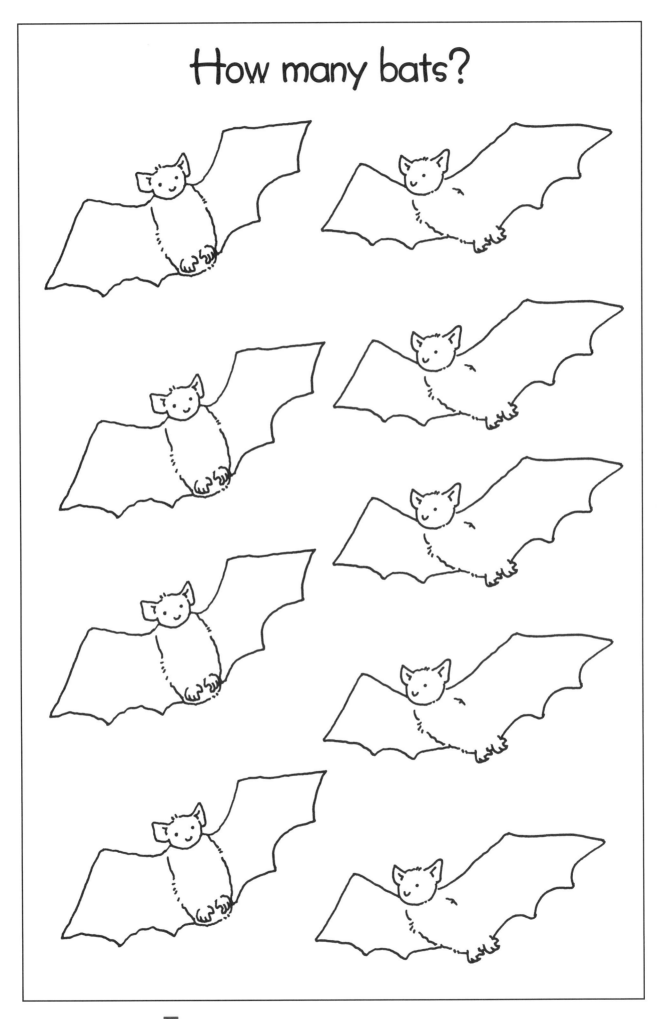

Exploring 6 – 10 **9** *Blake Education Reproducible*

How many cats?

Feed the Frogs

| S1,2 | C3,5 | N1,3,4 | O1,2,3 | WM1,2 |

Resources:
"Feed the Frogs" BLM, scissors, crayons, empty matchboxes, paste, feltpens, plastic counters, dot/number word cards 1-9.

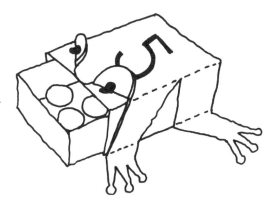

BLM

Activity A:
Work in groups of nine children. GROUP

Colour, cut out and paste a frog's body to an empty matchbox.
Each set of nine frogs may be a different colour.

Fold up the eyes and draw in half an eye on the paper and the other half on the box itself.

Fold the legs to create the rest of the frog's body.
Write a number from 1-9 on each of the nine frogs.
Alternatively, write the number words "one" to "nine" too!

Activity B:
Children feed the frogs by placing the matching number of counters into PAIR
each frog's mouth then pushing the mouth closed.

Children check each other's efforts (eg. Place the matching dot card beside each frog and match the counters to the dots).

Children may like to construct frogs for feeding in higher numbers of counters too!

Activity C:
Take two frogs at random.
Which one has more counters to eat?
Check by counting the counters.

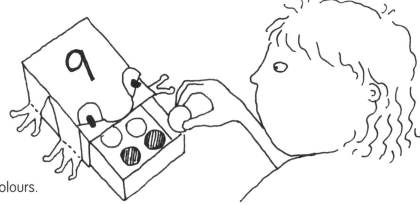

Activity D:
Place the frogs into counting order from
1-9 or backwards from 9-1.

Activity E:
Feed each frog counters in two different colours.
Discuss the combinations discovered.
eg. 7 and 2 for the "9" frog.

Activity F:
Emphasise mathematical language by asking/giving oral instructions to the group. CLASS
eg. "Hold up a frog which eats more then 5 counters." (6, 7, 8 or 9 ...) "Which frog eats fewer than four but more than 2 counters?" "Which two frogs together eat 7 counters?" (eg. 6 and 1, 3 and 4 ...) Discuss alternative solutions.

Activity G:
Make up your own "Feed the Frogs" activity.

Feed the frogs

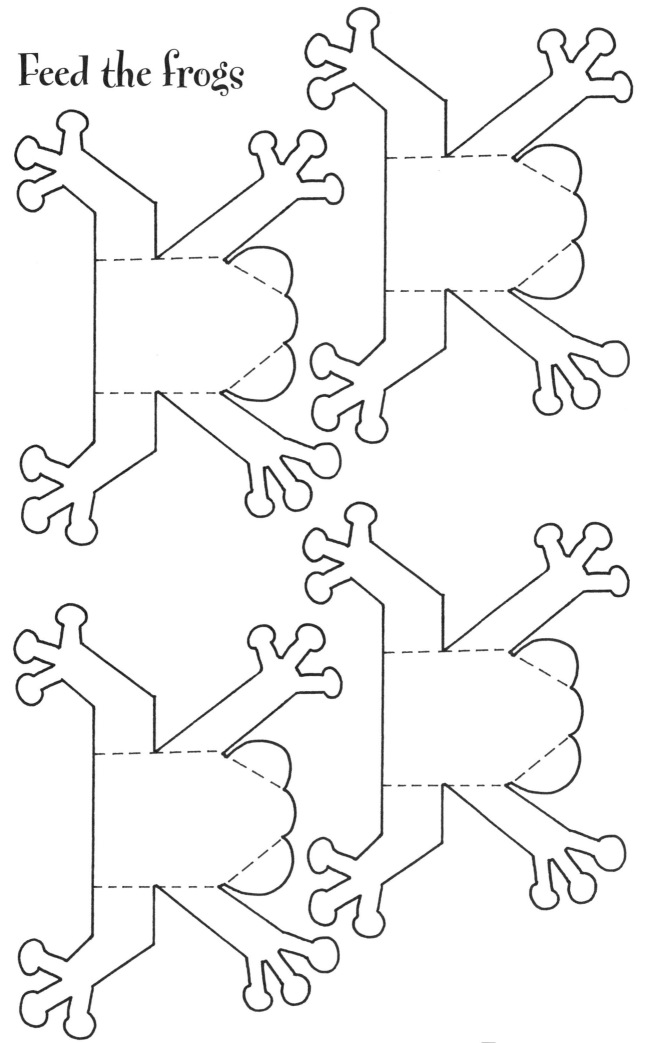

Beanbag Toss

C3 | N3,4 | O1

Resources:
Chalk, a beanbag for each pair of children.

Activity:
Discuss tally marks. Discuss how you make a "5" by placing a line through a "IIII". Children draw their own 3 x 3 grid with chalk on the playground. (It should be about 1 x 1 metre). Next draw in each of the numerals from 1-9 at random.

Stand back. Take turns to toss the beanbag onto the grid. Make a tally mark next to the number it lands on, or record on paper. Repeat for 9 throws each. Do some numbers score more than others? Compare your results with another team. Discuss. Can you make the beanbag land on each of the numbers in turn from 1-9? From 9-1?

Is it a fair share?

C3 | O4 | WM1,2

Resources:
A mixture of 9 small objects for each pair of children.

Activity:
Work with a partner. Take a handful of objects and count them together (eg. 7). If you share these with your partner, will it be a fair share? Guess first then check. Share up to 9 objects one by one between you and your partner until there are no more left to share. Count how many objects in each person's pile. Is it a fair share? What will you do with any extras that can't be shared? Repeat with other handfuls. Try to predict correctly whether the share will be fair or not (even or odd numbers). Explain why you think the share will/won't be fair.

Make it Nine

CLASS

C3,4 | N3,4 | WM1,2

Resources:
"Make it Nine" BLM, pencils.

BLM

Activity:
Discuss the pictures. Look at the beanstalk. Draw nine leaves. (How many are on the left? How many are on the right?)
Look at the egg carton. Colour in exactly nine eggs. Write the number on the left of the lid which shows you how many coloured eggs altogether. How many eggs do you have uncoloured? Write the number on the right of the lid which shows you how many eggs are not coloured.
Point to the domino. How many dots are there? Draw more dots on the right so that there are nine dots altogether.
Look at the numbers at the bottom of the page - three are missing. Write in the missing numbers. Look at the space under these numbers. Do you remember how to make tally marks? I'm going to clap my hands. Make a tally mark for each clap. (Clap 9 times, slowly).

On the back, draw a shape which has exactly nine sides. What might be a good name for this? Write the number which tells you how many sides.

Make it Nine

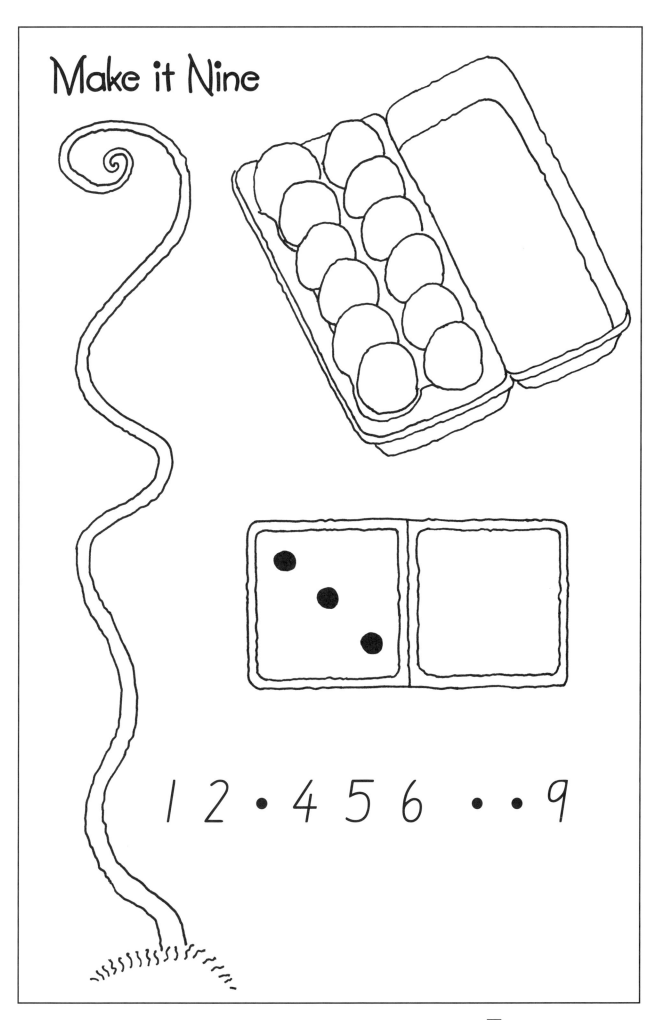

1 2 • 4 5 6 • • 9

Exploring

O

zero

Exploring 6 – 10 **0** *Blake Education Reproducible*

Guess

Guess how many elephants
Are hiding in this room.
Guess how many dinosaurs
Can jump across the moon.
Guess how many grasshoppers
Can lift their legs and run.
I'll tell you how many -
There's nought, there's zero, there's none.

What can you see?

Resources:

A poster of interest to the class, "Guess" BLM (p.65).

Activity: A

Discuss the poster. Ask questions related to objects which do and don't appear eg. "How many cats can you see?" "How many people?" "How many dogs?" (none) "How could we write that as a number?" (0) "What does it mean?" (there aren't any things there ...)
"Think of another counting question that has "none" as the answer" (how many people are wearing sunglasses?). Recite the "Guess" rhyme together.

Activity: B

Draw some shapes on the board. Ask individual children to come to the board and follow the instructions. eg. "Sam, draw a circle around the shape that has four sides." "Gina, draw nothing inside the triangle." (... mix up things that can and can't be done ...)

Activity: C

Write a list of words to describe nothing eg. "none", "nought", "zero", "nothing". Discuss the numeral "0". Develop a large class book with magazine pictures and a written commentary underneath (eg. "There are no cars on this road")

none
nought
zero
nothing

Sandpaper Numbers

Resources:

Sandpaper numerals from 0-9 glued to A5 size black (odd) and red (even) cards, sandtrays.

Activity: A

Discuss the "0" card. Demonstrate how to draw it starting at the top right and pulling down in an anticlockwise curve to join up at the top right again. Draw a small arrow showing where to start on the card. What does this shape remind the children of in real life? (eg. a squashed balloon, a football ...).

Demonstrate how to trace the sandpaper numeral with your index finger. Revise the starting points for each of the numerals 1-9. Draw in the starting arrow on each card.

Ask someone to close their eyes, feel the sandpaper shape on a card and guess the number just by feeling the numeral.

Use these cards at any time to reinforce the correct starting points.

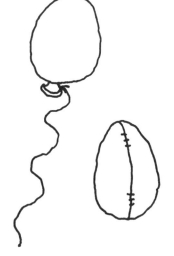

Activity: B

Practise writing 0s in the sand trays. Revise, practise how to write all of the digits 0-9. Make patterns with each numeral.

So many Numbers

 GROUP | S1,2 | N3,4 | WM3 | O1 |

Resources:

Magazines, newspapers, scissors, paste, A3 paper.

Activity:

Children work in 10 teams. Each team is given a number from 0-9. Try to find as many different written examples of this numeral in the magazines and newspapers. Paste these together on a large sheet of paper. When completed, put the pages together as a class number reference book.

Discuss some of the examples found. Which one is the largest? The smallest? The strangest? How many examples of each number did you collect altogether?

Dress me up

 GROUP | S1,2,4 | N3,4 | O1 | WM1,2 |

Resources:

"Dress me up" BLMs (photocopy 3 sets of 10 bodies - each set could be a different colour - and enough clothes to have a shirt and pants or skirt for each body card), scissors, small dot/numeral/word cards 0-9 (see p.3).

 BLM

Activity: A

Revise the dot/numeral/word cards 0-9. Write a number word from "zero" to "nine" on each body. Draw a matching set of dots on the pants/skirt and a matching numeral on the shirt.

Activity: B

Children mix up the clothes in each set then try to dress each person with the matching set of clothes as fast as they can.

Activity: C

Match a complete set from 0 to 9. Now mix up some of the clothes. Can the children identify the incorrect clothes?

Activity: D

Sort the bodies into counting order, forwards or backwards, then find the matching clothes.

Activity: E

Make a new set of bodies to include numbers up to 18. Children place a top in one colour and a bottom in another colour onto a body which shows the total number shown on the clothes.

eg. and go with

Dress me up

Dress me up

Number Hunt

| S1,2,4 | C3 | N2,3,4 | WM1,2,3 |

PAIR

Activity:
Divide the class into pairs (extra children can make a team of three). Each team decides on a really unusual item they will try to find on the Number Hunt. (eg. a red piece of paper, an old sandwich, a flat stone ...). Encourage creative, yet feasible, selections. Predict how many of this item they will discover. Write or draw a picture of the item on a scrap of paper.

Each team then walks around the area (eg. the playground ...) searching for their item. Tallies can be kept. Discuss the findings. Did all teams succeed in finding something? Were some items more common than others? Why were some items not found? Which items were found the most?

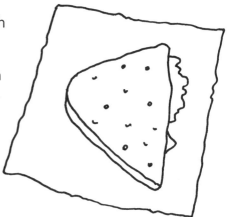

What's on your forehead?

| S4 | N4 | O3 | WM1,2 |

Resources:
Small yellow "Post It notes", or small pieces of paper (eg.2 x 5 cm) with a loop of cellotape behind each one, crayons/pencils.

PAIR

Activity:
Children work with a partner. Each person secretly writes one number from 0-9 onto his/her paper, then attaches this to his/her partner's forehead. Children try to guess their attached secret number by asking each other questions. Questions can only be answered with a "Yes" or a "No". Encourage the class to use terms like "higher than ..." or "smaller than ...". Can each person discover his/her secret number in fewer than five guesses?

Jump ahead

GROUP

| N3,4 | WM3 |

Resources:
"Jump ahead" BLM enlarged to A3, 4 small counters, "Spinner 0-9" BLM for each team, cardboard, scissors, paste, small skewer/match (photocopy the spinner onto cardboard, or paste the photocopy onto card and cut out, place the match/skewer through the centre and spin it to check its reliability).

BLM

Activity:
In teams of 4, take turns to spin the spinner. Move your counter to the next available matching number word. Try to be the first player to reach the head of the worm.

Jump ahead

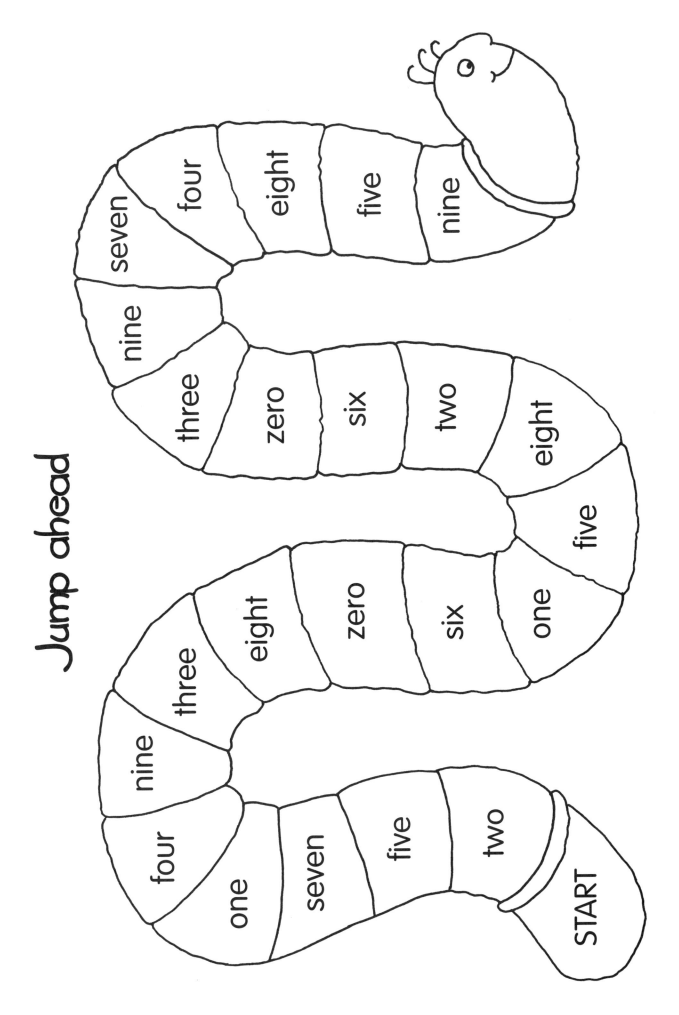

Spinners
0 – 9

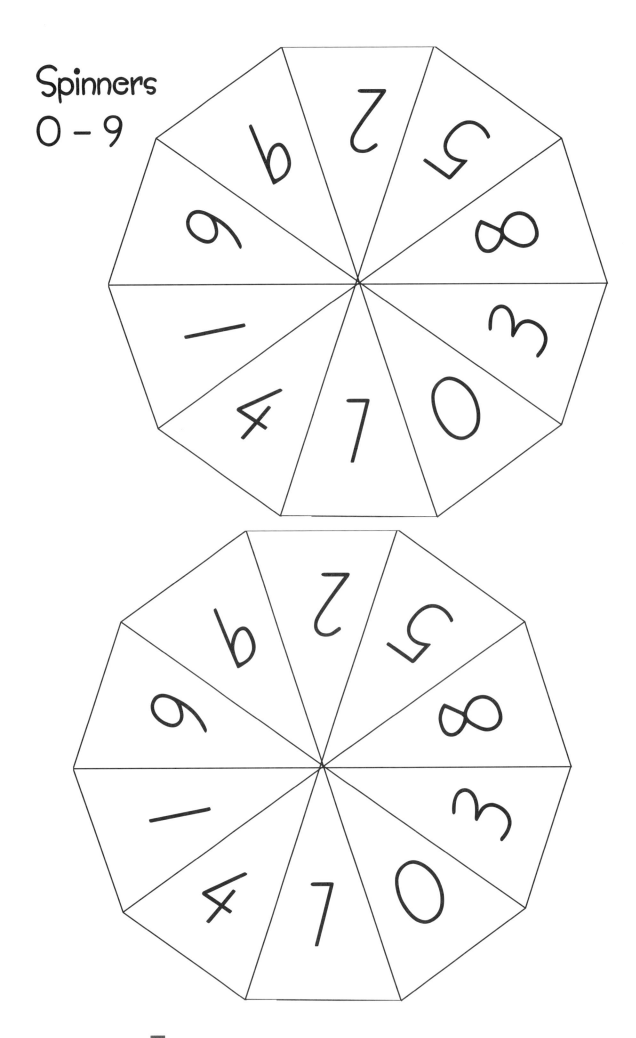

Simon says ...

 C3 | N3 | WM3

Activity:

Whole class game, which starts with everyone standing up. Select one child to be the leader. Call the game after his/her name (eg. Fatima: "Fatima says ...").

The leader calls out some number instructions for the rest of the class to follow (eg. "Fatima says: do 5 starjumps ... 3 kneebends, no headshakes ...) Children who respond on the "0" instructions sit down. Continue until no children can be tricked, or until there are only 10 children left standing.

Tell me a story

 CLASS N3 | WM2,3

Activity:

Whole class game. Retell class news, popular stories, rhymes or sing songs, where some of the characters in the first few lines are removed (eg. "Yesterday was my birthday and I didn't get any presents!" "My cat had no kittens and we were all very excited." "Once upon a time there were no bears." "Snow White and No Dwarves.") Discuss the consequences of such changes and how different the world would be if we didn't have numbers to help us communicate.

Sort the Mail Memory

 GROUP

Resources:

"Sort the Mail" BLMs (photocopy the mailboxes onto cardboard, colour then laminate; photocopy the envelopes onto cardboard, or paste the photocopy onto card, laminate and cut out as individual envelopes; place the envelopes into a small plastic container with a lid).

 BLM

Activity:

Form teams of 3 players with a game board each. Mix up the envelopes face down. Take turns to turn over three cards. If two or more cards match, place them on the matching mailbox on your board. If they do not match, turn them face down again. If on a later turn you find an envelope which matches two others already on your board, you can keep this to make a full mailbox. Try to be the first person with three full mailboxes!

Make up your own rules for a "Sort the Mail" game.

S1,2,4 | N3 | O1 | WM2,3

Sort the Mail

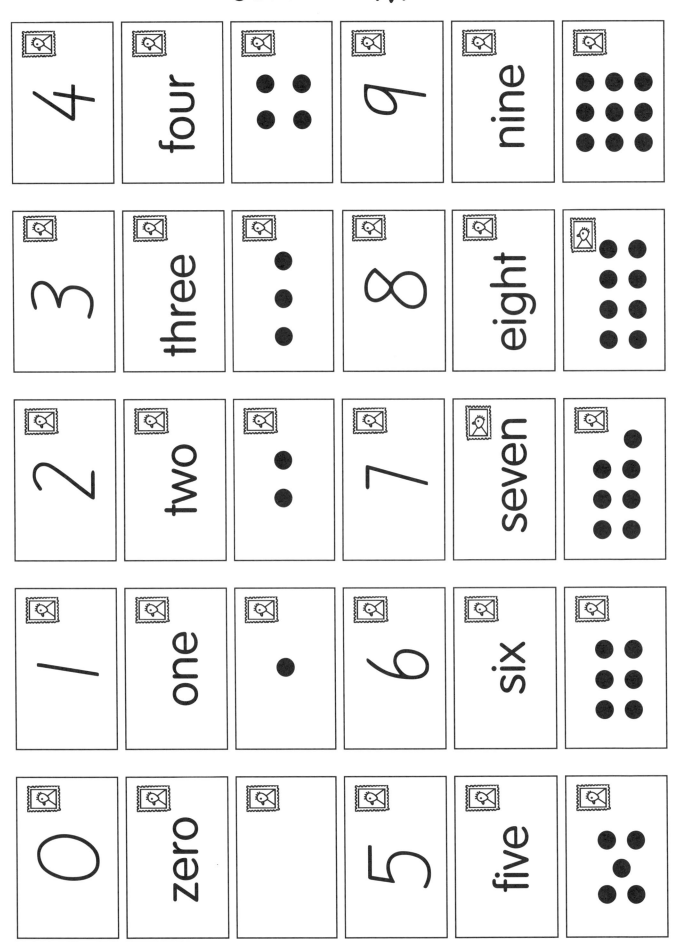

Exploring 6 – 10 **0** *Blake Education Reproducible*

Sort the Mail

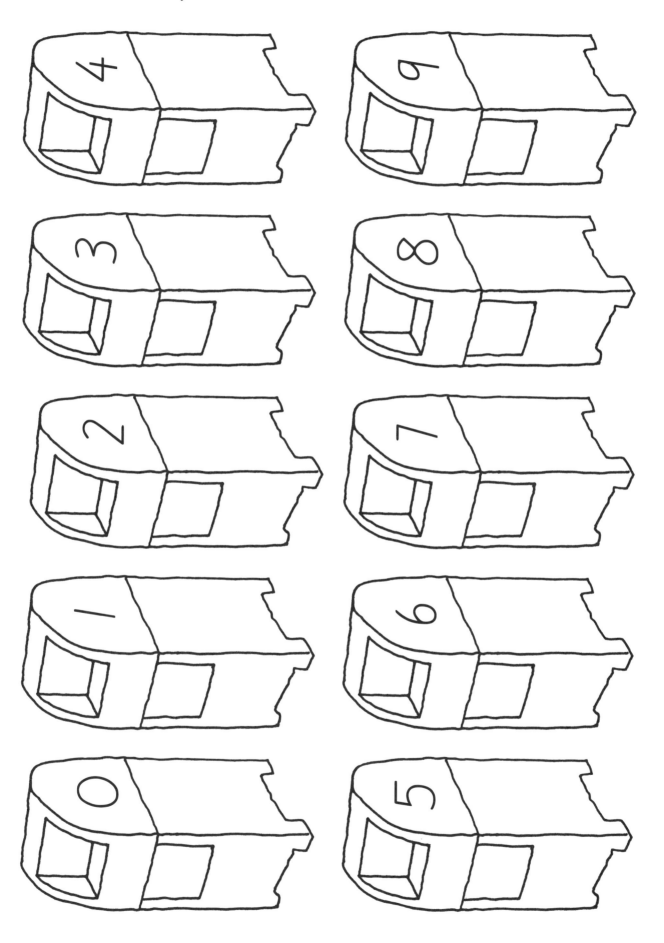

Exploring

10

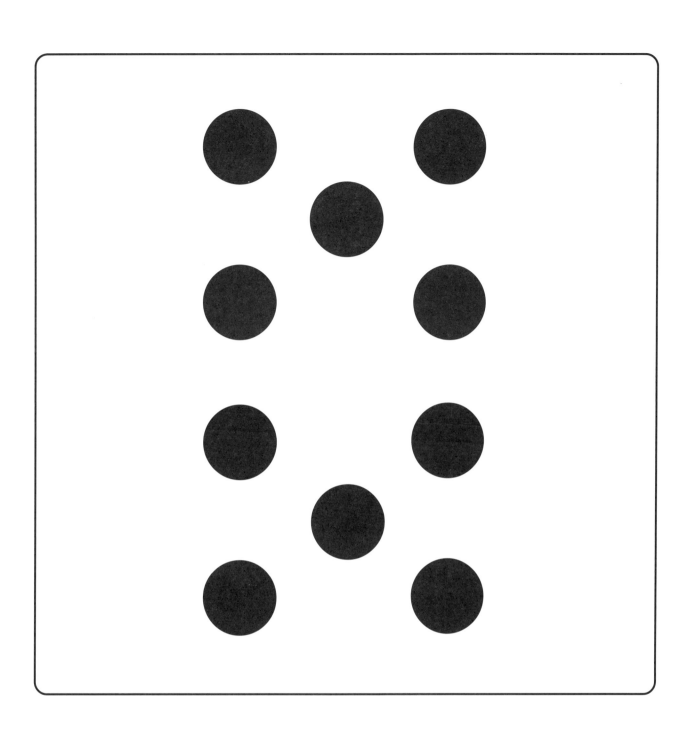

ten

Exploring 6 – 10 **10** *Blake Education Reproducible*

Ten little astronauts

10 9 8 7 6 5 4 3 2 1 0 *Blast off!*
Ten little astronauts went to the moon,
Where they danced and played all day.
Ten little astronauts were called back home soon,
But how many decided to stay?

What's so special?

 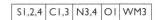

Resources:
A set of large 0-10 domino dot/word and numeral cards.

Activity:
Discuss the cards for 10. What is so special about this number? Encourage the children to respond creatively (eg. "It comes after 9 ", "I live at No. 10 " ...) Discuss in particular how this is the first number that uses two of the numbers we have been studying - 1 and 0. How many birthdays before they are 10 years old? Do they have any stories/songs/rhymes they know about 10? (eg. "10 green bottles", "There were 10 in the bed ..." "Ten little Indians" ...). Mix up the cards and sort into counting order.

Fingers

Resources:
Paper, crayons.

Activity: A
Two children demonstrate how to trace around a partner's outstretched hands on the chalkboard. How many fingers altogether? Discuss and count aloud. Next ask individual children to come to the front to write a number from 1-10 on each finger starting on the left.

Activity: B
Form pairs. Take turns to trace each other's fingers onto paper and write in the numbers in order.

Show me your antennae

Resources:
A set of large 0-10 cards.

Activity: A
Start with your fingers hiding behind your head. Imagine you are a creature from outer space. You have 10 antennae altogether but at any one time you can have none or up to all of them showing! Show me 10 antennae (Hold up 10 fingers above your head). Show me 5 (Hold up 5 fingers above your head). Show me none (hands on heads). Ask individual children to call out instructions too.

Activity: B
Hold up a numeral card at random. Children race to show a matching number of antennae (fingers). How many antennae not showing?

Activity: C
Work with a partner. Hold up a number of antennae (fingers) at random for about three seconds, then hide them. Your partner guesses how many antennae he/she saw. Reveal your fingers and count them together. Swap roles.

Toes

CLASS

| S1,2 | C1,3 | N3,4 |

PAIR

Resources:
Paper, crayons.

Activity:
Repeat the activities for "Fingers" but this time use your toes, with shoes/socks removed!

Build a Beanstick

GROUP

| C1,3,5 | N,3,7 | O1,3 | WM2 |

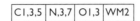

Resources:
Dried beans, paddle-pop sticks, craft glue, 1-6 die.

Activity: A
Game for 4 players. Imagine you are farmers. Every time you get 10 beans you will plant them in a straight row by gluing them to a paddle-pop stick. Take turns to throw the die and take the corresponding number of beans. Every time you collect 10 beans you can glue them to a stick. Any extra beans are left loose until the next group of 10 beans is formed. At the end of the game, count up how many sticks you have altogether. Can you count how many beans altogether?

Activity: B
Once plenty of beansticks have been created, you can change the rules of the game so that once 10 beans are collected they can be swapped for a beanstick. That way you won't have to keep buying more beans!

Build a Bundle

GROUP

| C1,3,5 | N3,7 | O1,3 | WM2 |

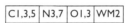

Resources:
Used matchsticks (preferably the brightly coloured craft ones), rubber bands, 1-6 die.

Activity:
Game for 4 players. Play as for "Build a Beanstick" but this time imagine you are farmers cutting sugar-cane. Every time you get 10 sticks of sugar-cane (matches), you can tie them in a bundle with a rubber band.

Clothes Pegs

GROUP

| N3 | O1,3 | WM1,2,3 |

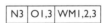

Resources:
Plastic pegs, washing line, tea towels.

Activity: A
How many different ways can you peg up two tea towels using exactly 10 pegs? Discuss. Ask for suggestions. Demonstrate. Can you peg up "0" and "10"? (Yes! You could fold the tea towel over the line using no pegs at all ...)

Activity: B
How many different ways can you peg up three tea towels using exactly 10 pegs? Discuss alternative strategies together.

Domino Dots to 10

Resources:
A set of dominoes for each group.

Activity:
Try to place the dominoes so that all the dots in one line add up to 10. Place a domino sideways to start a new line. How many groups of 10 can you create? Find a way to record your discoveries.

eg.

Crazy Caterpillar

Resources:
4 "Caterpillar" BLMs, storage envelope, 1-6 die for each group.

Activity A:
Work in groups of 4. Colour a gameboard each (then laminate). Colour a set of 10 caterpillar legs each, (laminate), then cut out as individual legs to make 40 legs altogether. Store the legs in an envelope.

Activity B:
Game for 4 players. Place the legs in the centre of the group. Take turns to throw the die, take that many legs and place them on your caterpillar. Try to be the first person to have all ten legs attached. You must throw exactly the right number to collect ten legs (eg. if you have 8 legs already, you need to throw a 2).

Activity C:
Play a subtraction version by placing all ten legs on your caterpillar at the start of the game. Remove the matching number of legs each time you throw the die.

What's the Time?

Resources:
"What's the Time" BLM (enlarged to A3 size) for each pair.

Activity:
Discuss "o'clock" and telling time on the hour. Colour, (laminate), cut out as ten individual clocks. Sort the clocks into counting order starting with 1 o'clock. Which clock is next in time order?

Variation?
Cover up the clock numerals. Can you tell the correct time just by looking at the position of the clock hands? Can you sort the clocks into time order like this?

Crazy Caterpillar

Crazy Caterpillar Legs

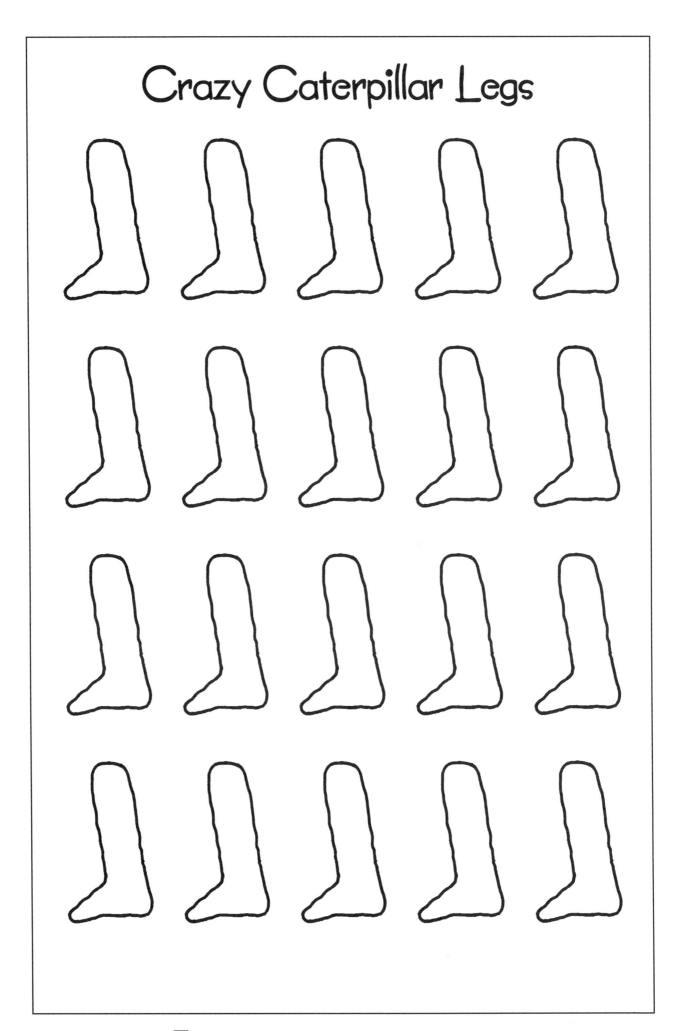

What's the Time?

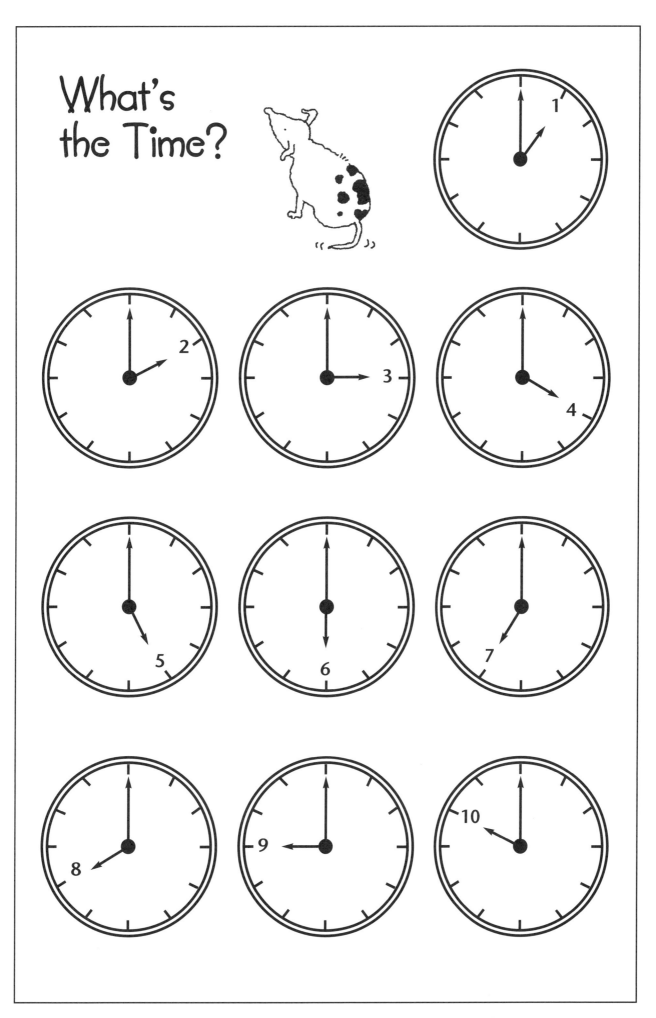

Counting 0-10 in other languages

CLASS

C1 | WM3

Resources:
"Blast Off" BLM (enlarged to A3 or more). **BLM**

Activity:
Ask children in the class who can speak additional languages to teach you how they count from 1-10 or 0-10. Count forwards and backwards using the Blast Off poster as a stimulus.

How many Astronauts?

 GROUP   C1,2,4,5 | O1,2

Resources:
See "Ten little astronauts" rhyme (p. 79), "Blast Off" BLM (enlarged to A3).

 BLM

Activity:
Whole class activity. Discuss the Blast Off poster. Practise counting backwards aloud. Discuss the number rhyme. Read aloud. Select 10 children to be the astronauts to act out the story. The astronauts go outside and wait by the door, or go behind a screen where they can't be seen in the classroom, as the rest of the class say the rhyme together. After "But how many decided to stay?", the teacher, or a child from the class, knocks on the door 10 times and calls for the astronauts to come home. The 10 hidden children decide amongst themselves how many to send back in (eg.7). Seven children walk back in and stand in front of the class. The class now guesses how many astronauts must be left behind on the moon. Count the number of children -1 2 3 4 5 6 7. Now count on until you reach ten - 8 9 10 (3 children must be outside). Ask the remaining astronauts to come inside and check the guesses.

Variation?
Repeat with any number of astronauts from 5-10 (or more). Change the number word and the number of knocks to match the new number.

Alien Footprints

 CLASS   C1,2 | S1,2 | N3,4,6

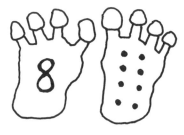

Resources:
"Alien Footprints" BLM (make 11 copies). **BLM**

Activity:
Write a number from 0-10 on each left footprint. Draw in some marks (eg. dots) on the right footprint (You could also make footprints for larger numbers). Colour, laminate, cut out as individual footprints. Store in a plastic container with a lid.

How to play?
Invent a story about some mysterious marks found on the craters by astronauts. They could belong to aliens. What might the creature look like based on its footprint? Mix up all the footprints. Sort them into counting order from 0-10, with matching left and right feet.

Variation?
Sort them into odd and even. Sort them backwards from 10-0. Hide several footprints. Can you find the missing number?

Alien Footprints

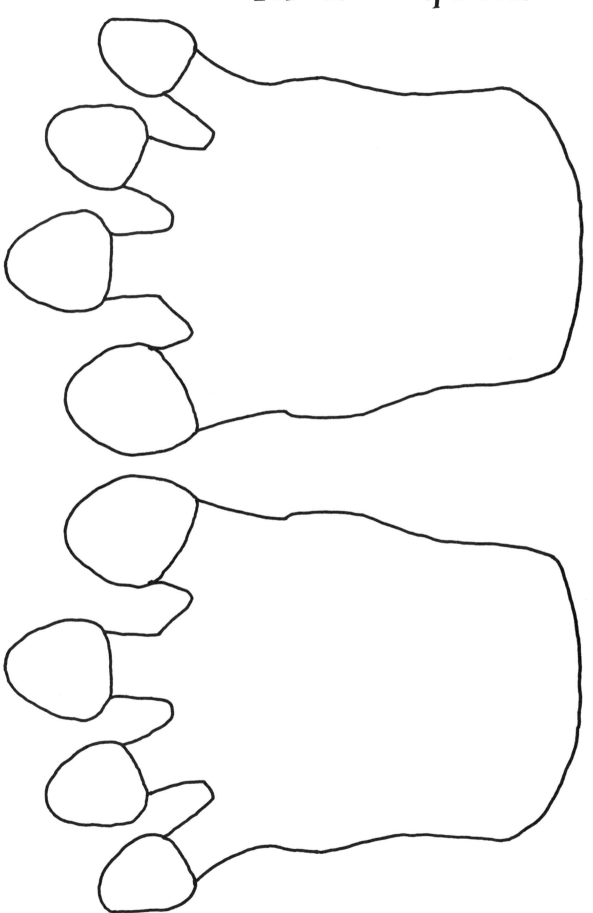

BLAST OFF !

Finding out what they can do

Throughout Exploring 6-10, any of the activities can serve as practical tasks for assessment purposes or become part of each student's portfolio. The end-of-unit worksheet shown here, however, can be used as a checkup at the start of the units or as revision at the end. You will need a copy of the worksheet and a pencil for each child. Written examples of teachers' comments have been added for your use. Feel free to copy and modify these to suit your needs.

What will you say?

Sorting, Counting
| S1 | C3 |

Look at the line of children. How many are wearing shorts? Write this number on the left. How many are wearing a skirt? Write this number on the right.

Sample Profile Comments
"Amelia can sort and count up to 10 objects and record this as a numeral. We're still working on her concepts of left or right!"

Counting, Numeration
| C3,4 | N4,6 |

Look at the children again. Look at the numbers on the shirts. Write in the missing numbers on the shirts to show how you count backwards.

Sample Profile Comments
"Elizabeth writes the numerals 0-10 in correct formation and in counting order forwards or backwards."

Look at the flowers. Count how many petals on each one. Write this number in the centre of each flower. Colour in the petals only if the flower has an odd number of petals.

Sample Profile Comments
"Taso has developed a strategy for identifying odd or even numbers. He can match numbers to sets of objects up to 10 to show how many altogether."

Turn your page over. Write your own story about 10 things and draw 10 things to match.

Sample Profile Comments
"Bridget clearly relates the numbers from 1-10 to her own life. She is an imaginative story-teller!"

Turn your page over again. Draw a small shape with 6 sides in the bottom right corner. Draw nothing inside your shape. Write the number that tells you how many things are inside this shape!

Sample Profile Comments
"Khan grasps the concept of zero. He also makes good attempts at drawing specified geometric shapes."

Operations
| O1,2 |

Look at the cats. Count them. Draw some more cats so that there are 7 cats altogether. Look at the spiders. Count them. Cross out some spiders until there are 9 spiders left uncrossed.

Sample Profile Comments
"Samantha demonstrates a competent understanding of simple addition and subtraction at this level."

Exploring numbers to Ten

Outcome Indicators Record Sheet

EXPLORING NUMBERS 6-10

NAME

Sorting	S1	Sorts and classifies objects into two or more sets.
	S2	Explains the sorting criterion for a given set.
	S3	Identifies similarities and differences in objects and sets.
	S4	Places objects into order by size, shape or number.
Counting	C1	Rote counts forwards to …
	C2	Rote counts backwards from…
	C3	Counts collections up to …
	C4	Identifies missing numbers in a counting sequence.
	C5	Counts on from a given number.
Numeration	N1	Compares & orders sets of objects using one-to-one correspondence.
	N2	Estimates size of sets - bigger, smaller, the same.
	N3	Represents 1 - 10 with objects/drawings.
	N4	Reads writes and orders numerals and number words to 10.
	N5	Reads, orders and uses ordinal numbers and words to "tenth".
	N6	Identifies a group of objects as odd or even.
Operations	O1	Demonstrates understanding of simple addition.
	O2	Demonstrates understanding of simple subtraction.
	O3	Creates, records own number questions from stories & real-life situations.
	O4	Demonstrates understanding of simple fractions as "equal shares" .
Patterning	P1	Identifies, predicts and continues a given pattern.
	P2	Creates their own counting patterns.
	P3	Records patterns by writing or drawing.
Working mathematically	WM1	Explains or demonstrates how they reached their answers.
	WM2	Solves number problems using a variety of strategies.
	WM3	Uses numbers as part of everyday life.
	WM4	Uses a calculator to explore numbers.

Mathematics Topics for 5 year olds

SAMPLE YEARLY PROGRAM SUGGESTIONS

Week	Term 1	Term 2	Term 3	Term 4
1	Prenumber	Exploring 5	Chance/Data	Chance/Data
2	Prenumber	Length	Exploring 9	Early Fractions
3	Space: 3D	Exploring 6	Exploring 6	Length
4	Exploring 1	Time	Exploring 0	Early Addition/Subtraction
5	Space: 3D	Exploring 7	Space: 3D	Area
6	Exploring 2	Mass	Space: 2D	Time
7	Space: 2D	Temperature	Time	Mass/Volume
8	Exploring 3	Exploring 8	Exploring 10	Space: Position
9	Space: 2D	Money	Volume	Revision
10	Exploring 4	Revision	Revision	Revision

Total number of weeks

Space: 8   Measurement: 10   Number: 16   Chance/Data: 2   Revision: 4

Sample Weekly Program

STRAND Number
GRADE K

SUBSTRAND Numeration (Exploring 7)
TERM 2 **WEEK** 5

OUTCOMES

- sorts/draws objects into groups of 7
- puts groups of 1 - 7 objects into counting order
- matches numerals to groups of 7 objects
- puts numeral cards 1-7 into counting order
- states the number of objects in groups up to 7
- states the order of an object from 1st to 7th

LANGUAGE

- "more than ...", "fewer than ...."
- "the same number as ...."
- "as many as ", "not enough"
- "there's ... altogether in this group"
- "this one has the smallest number of objects in it"

RESOURCES

"Snow White" book
numeral cards 1-7
1st to 7th cards
1-7 spinners

paint in 7 rainbow colours
brushes
0-7 dot cards
paper bags

building bricks:
(DUPLO, multilink,
cuisenaire rods ...)
gold bottle tops

playdough
cookie cutters
BLM photocopies
scissors, crayons

MONDAY	TUESDAY	WEDNESDAY	THURSDAY	FRIDAY
• Read "Snow White". Discuss/role play Snow White and the 7 Dwarfs.	• General discussion of rainbows and 7 colours	• "What day is it?"	• Rotating Group Activities (5 minutes):	• "The Dwarfs' Challenge"
• Discuss numeral for 7. Write in air. Sort 1-7 cards into order.	• Rotating Group Activities (10 minutes):	• "Weekly Jobs for Dwarfs"	"What a lot of stairs"	• Free activities related to 7
• Discuss "7th". Sort 1st to 7th cards into order.	"Colour a rainbow"	• "Snow White's Week"	"What a lot of bricks"	(eg. Design your own jewellery, How Hairy, Press and Guess, 7 letter words, 7-sided shapes on geoboards, drawing 7-pointed stars ...)
• Role play number rhyme "7 Dwarfs".	"Rainbow Dwarfs"	• How many fingers? Finish with fast whole class game using random numeral cards. Children hold up fingers to match.	"Mining for gold"	
	• How many dots? Finish with fast whole class estimation game using random dot cards.		"Snow White's cookies"	• Role play number rhyme "7 Dwarfs".
			• How many in a Huggle? Finish with fast whole class game using random numeral cards. Children form groups (huggles) to match.	

Exploring 6-10 Index